ALL ABOUT
BACTERIA

Ravi Mantha is a health writer and activist. After eighteen years as a professional investor, Ravi realized that life is not just about jet-setting and making boatloads of money (although there is no harm in doing that), it is also about doing something to improve society.

Ravi has spent several years researching the latest advances in health and the human body; this book is a result of that effort. *All About Bacteria* promotes alternative health backed by scientific research, bringing together two concepts that were until now seen as incompatible.

Born and raised in India, he has spent over two decades in the US and London, and currently lives in Singapore. You can read his health blog at www.ravionhealth.com.

ALL ABOUT
BACTERIA

Ravi Mantha

Collins
An Imprint of HarperCollins Publishers

First published in India in 2013 by Collins
An imprint of HarperCollins *Publishers* India

Copyright © Ravi Mantha 2013

ISBN: 978-93-5029-404-8

2 4 6 8 10 9 7 5 3 1

HarperCollins *Publishers*
A-53, Sector 57, Noida, Uttar Pradesh 201301, India
77-85 Fulham Palace Road, London W6 8JB, United Kingdom
Hazelton Lanes, 55 Avenue Road, Suite 2900, Toronto, Ontario M5R 3L2
and 1995 Markham Road, Scarborough, Ontario M1B 5M8, Canada
25 Ryde Road, Pymble, Sydney, NSW 2073, Australia
31 View Road, Glenfield, Auckland 10, New Zealand
10 East 53rd Street, New York NY 10022, USA

Typeset in 11.5/15 Minion Pro by
R. Ajith Kumar

Printed and bound at
Thomson Press (India) Ltd

To my wife

CONTENTS

❧

CONTENTS

FOREWORD

❧❧❧

This book is intended to improve our understanding of our health and body by combining historical perspectives on medicine with the latest on-going research. I have attempted to build a narrative that not only explains how the human body works, but also shows us how we can make simple changes in our day-to-day life to enhance our health and heal common ailments.

I am writing this not as a scientist but as an inquisitive individual. Science has become so specialized these days that sometimes it takes a generalist to connect all the dots of scientific discovery taking place every day. This book attempts to do just that.

While there are many scientists who are working diligently on increasing our understanding of our body, our human ecosystem and our health, it should also be noted that plenty of scientific research today is funded and controlled by special interests that usually have the goal of selling you something. As you will see in this book, I have the opposite aim. Every solution you will find in this book is designed to keep you healthy, and these home solutions mean that your money will stay in your wallets at the same time.

It is not at all my intention to attempt to discredit 'germ theory', which holds that microorganisms are the cause of infectious diseases. This theory is one of the foundations of modern medicine and has helped save millions of lives by developing treatments and sanitation techniques to fight pathogenic strains of bacteria. My goal is to modify germ theory, by differentiating between pathogenic strains of bacteria and good strains, in order to understand our relationship with bacteria better. This book is also interested in the mechanisms that turn everyday bacteria into pathogens, and in trying to stop them from doing so. I will suggest avenues for future research, and areas where public health policy may be better served by a different approach.

This is not a new-age tome. I aim to place this book firmly within the realm of the scientific method, citing published works where appropriate. I will try to differentiate fact from conjecture and anecdotes from statistical evidence. But science itself is a process of discovery, hypothesis, conjecture, testing and finally proof. In the field of microbiology, which relates to human health, the priority has been to fight 'bugs' rather than understand how the bacterial-human symbiosis works. This is also an unfortunate by-product of modern medicine's obsession with curing and managing diseases, instead of focusing on preventing them.

I have a bold ambition, to argue the case for a unified symbiotic theory of germs and humans, where we see human-symbiotic germs not just as partners but as extensions of our own body, fit to be accorded the status of a vital organ.

As many ideas in this book are still under research, I reserve the right to alter my views as more conclusive facts become available. When future scientific research proves my conjectures to be either facts or falsehoods, I will do my best to reflect the change, both in the online media and in future editions.

Fond wishes and good health!
Ravi Mantha

INTRODUCTION

WE ARE MOSTLY A BACTERIAL SOUP

Newsflash: Scientists have discovered that of the cells that make up our body, 90 per cent are bacteria. Now look at yourself in the mirror. Can you see them? Every inch of your body, inside and outside, is covered by billions of the little critters.[1]

Of the 100 trillion cells that make up the human body, only 10 per cent are what we would call human cells. Since we are also 65 per cent water, if an alien civilization were to capture one of us and stick us under a microscope, they would rightly conclude that we are basically a walking bacterial soup.

Before you shudder in disgust and head for the shower, hold on for a minute and think this through. You would not be alive without these bacterial cells any more than you would be without the human cells. The microbial ecosystem that envelops your body is so important to your well-being that we should start calling it a vital organ. Let's call this vital organ the 'human symbiote', a loose collective of several thousand species of bacteria made up of billions of individual members. This vital organ has just as much interest in keeping us healthy as any other organ in our body.

Now that we have identified this new vital organ, there are lots of questions that we need to figure out. How does this symbiote work? What types of bugs does it comprise? What do they do? If it is like an organ, how can we take better care of it? And how come we didn't know anything about it before?

We are going to answer these questions and a few more as we go along, but we are going to need to change our mindset. We need to accept that bugs are not evil. I am going to show you that most microbes are harmless. In fact, the microbes that make up the human symbiote are powerful allies that constantly work to keep your body and mind healthy.

Let us start with our understanding of the symbiote and how this understanding has progressed in the last five years. Until recently, we believed that the bacteria that live on and in the human body numbered fifty or sixty different species. This is because the only way to count them was by taking a swab from an area of the body, and transferring it to a petri dish or agar plate. You then saw what grew in the petri dish. The problem with this approach is that only a minuscule number of the different kinds of bacteria that make up our symbiote actually grow in a petri dish. It's a bit like counting the number of stars by looking at the night sky, and concluding that there are only 3,000 stars in the whole universe!

With modern DNA sequencing techniques, we are now discovering that the number of bacterial species in our body is in the thousands. At least.

Western medicine has, until now, treated the bacterial symbiote not only with contempt, but with something akin to genocidal intent. We have misused our lack of understanding of the symbiote to declare war on it, and antibiotics are like nuclear weapons deployed in this war. A new approach is clearly needed to help us interact with our symbiote, and this book aims to provide a basic guide to doing this.

We humans have always been prone to the elementary mistake of looking at everything in binary terms, positive or negative, good or evil. Our desire to reduce complex problems into a simple plus or minus has completely poisoned our relation with our symbiote.

Our body is like a pond ecosystem. The clarity and purity of the water on the surface can be achieved only by having an ecosystem of thousands of species living in a healthy equilibrium below the surface. You can create the appearance of health in any pond by treating the water on the surface but this effect is temporary, it will disturb the pond ecosystem and eventually result in the destruction of this ecosystem.

But how did this ecosystem come into being in the human body, and what are the various roles it plays?

In modern medicine, over the last hundred years, bacteria were divided into two classes: primarily evil pathogens and a few good probiotic bacteria. Medicine and public policy focused on fighting the pathogens, mainly through antibiotics. This initially produced a miraculous improvement in public health and life expectancy and was undoubtedly the right approach to take at the time, given our lack of knowledge of the root causes of diseases as well as pathogen behaviour. But the forces of evolution are more powerful than anything medical science can come up with. Faced with widespread antibiotic use around the world, pathogens initially retreated but returned in more resistant forms.

It is now clear that it was not antibiotic use that curbed the spread of pathogens and improved life expectancy, but massive improvements in sanitation (which physically interrupted the transmission of epidemics) and public nutrition (which strengthened human bodies to fight off potential infections on their own). If we look at the major infectious diseases through history that are not caused by viruses, only a handful shows up as the big killers: tuberculosis, malaria, cholera, bubonic plague and typhoid. Of these diseases, tuberculosis is an illness caused by a weak immune system (historically a nutrition-related disease, now often associated with HIV), and the rest are controlled by public sanitation methods more than by medicines. Antibiotics help, but their effect is limited to curing individuals, not stopping the spread of epidemics. Better sanitation and nutrition are the true preventive measures, as they stop the easy spread of infectious diseases.

Think of antibiotics as firefighting tools, while sanitation can be compared to better building codes. Firefighting is of course very important when there is an actual fire, but if you look at the history of the twentieth century, many million more lives were saved because of improved building codes that prevented fires in the first place. The real life-savers then are not the glamorous firefighters of Western popular imagination, but the humble building inspectors who go about their business with quiet aplomb!

Antibiotics, sanitation and better nutrition are the three weapons that have helped us conquer bacterial epidemics, and have led to dramatic improvements in the average human lifespan. But today in the developed world, these improvements in sanitation and public nutrition have run their course. Public health focus regarding infectious diseases in the rich world has now shifted to viruses such as HIV and influenza. Meanwhile, antibiotics are being misused to such an extent that they are doing more harm than good.

Perhaps the most revealing discovery in the 'battle' against infection is the fact that many so-called pathogens are actually native species of the human symbiote. In other words, most of these bacteria live on or in our bodies, without causing any problems most of the time. Examples of these are bacteria that can cause meningitis (Neisseria meningitidis), dental disease (Streptococcus aureus), stomach disease (Enterococcus faecalis), diarrhoea (Escherichia coli), pneumonia (Streptococcus pneumoniae and Streptococcus pyogenes), and dangerous hospital-acquired infections (Staphylococcus aureus). Of these, Escherichia coli (E. coli) is the most common and hardy bacterium found on any surface where people live. Given how common it is, E. coli has developed resistance to every antibiotic that is currently in use, and a new approach is required to deal with it.

Since these bacteria are well adapted to the human symbiote, fighting illnesses caused by them via antibiotics is like a pointless arms race against ourselves. There is an alternate sustainable approach to controlling rogue bacteria, instead of the current futile efforts to annihilate them. We will also look at the problem of DNA transfer (a process involving microbes exchanging DNA material and acquiring characteristics from each other), which can lead a 'friendly member' of our symbiote to turn into a pathogenic strain.

A lot of new research concerning allergies is bearing fruit, especially on the interaction between the symbiote and the human body via the immune system. It is extremely important to realize that the immune system is in itself a significant disease agent, causing afflictions such as asthma, lupus, arthritis, endometriosis and food allergies. We also need to understand that not only can we be allergic to *something*, we can also be allergic because of the *lack of something*. For example, a mineral deficiency is also an allergy because your body is producing symptoms due to the absence of something.

Next time you go to a health food store and see things that are supposed to 'boost your immune system', you might want to question not only whether the product actually boosts your immune system, but whether it is a good idea to do so in the first place. Unless you are HIV positive or otherwise immune-compromised, the last thing you need to do is boost your immune system. Instead, improving the symbiote balance in your body is a much better area to focus on. We will look closely at how to do this.

Recognizing the symbiote as a friend and looking after it is an important step to well-being. But even this is a first step, and it turns out that scientists are discovering ever more complex ways in which bacteria affect the core of our personality itself. Is there a way that the symbiote can unleash specific behavioural changes within us? Can we become more creative by harnessing the symbiote? A tantalizing view from history shows a possible way forward by looking at how the bacterial symbiote in our body directly affects the brain.

Viruses are not very well understood by science, but are there viruses that are well adapted to the human body and play a role in good health? It turns out there are, and further, that viruses play a significant role in enhancing genetic diversity.

Finally, we will talk about how to approach the world around us, with a view to improving the symbiote balance and enhancing health. There is a whole new field called 'Nutraceutical' that addresses the needs of the symbiote for the first time, although there is a danger of the marketing hype running ahead of reality. Nutraceuticals are food or nutrition supplements that supposedly work to improve your health balance. These include compounds like resveratrol, which is found in red wine, and specific types of probiotic foods, which are meant to improve the bacterial balance in your gut. As we will see, the efficacy of these supplements is far from proven.

There are no cure-alls when it comes to human health. We are not clones but a 7-billion strong community of human hosts who are, in turn, composed of individually complex ecosystems with thousands of species and trillions of cells. If we look at human physiology as a whole and see how it has evolved over tens of thousands of years, it is clear that we are still a work in progress.

Evolution being a constant, there are remnants of evolutionary paths taken within human populations in our genetic make-up that have led to poor health. Disorders such as sickle-cell anaemia, juvenile diabetes, Huntington's disease and many other genetic diseases are examples of these evolutionary curve-balls. If left alone, nature will eventually eradicate many of these diseases from the human gene pool through natural selection, and new diseases may also be created during this endless process of trial and error. But modern medicine has interrupted this natural process by providing life extending treatments. This is a wonderful thing, but it also raises a number of challenges.

We have a lot of evolutionary baggage, remnants of disease and survival in our genes passed on from earlier eras, that has twisted our genes in different directions. People now survive with genetic diseases, lead more or less normal lives and even reproduce. This includes genetic diseases like juvenile diabetes that would have killed them in childhood had they been born even fifty years ago.

But there are many more diseases that can be said to be genetically pre-disposed, like Type 2 diabetes, heart disease and certain autoimmune disorders. Possessing certain genes increases the chances of being afflicted with these illnesses, but this is by no means automatic. Through a better management of the six big factors discussed in the concluding section of this book, one of which is our symbiote, it is possible to avoid these diseases. We can overcome our genetic predisposition in most cases.

The benefits of Western medicine are undeniable; millions of lives have been saved, and the quality of life has improved for billions of people. Life expectancy in countries with access to proper Western medicine has soared, and the vast majority of people can look forward to a greatly increased and healthy lifespan as compared to our human ancestors. Having said that, it is now clear that all the low-hanging fruit or health improvements from Western medicine have already been picked. Western medicine has given us eighty-year lifespans, but now a quarter of us will get diabetes, another quarter will get heart disease and a third quarter will get chronic lung, prostrate, kidney or liver ailments. Disease management has become extremely complex and expensive, and health care costs are soaring around the world to unaffordable levels. For the average citizen in a developed country, 80 per cent health care costs are consumed in the last two years of their life. Most of the time, this cost is to treat the cumulative effects of a lifetime of bad eating and living habits.

Given that increasing costs are providing less and less benefits to the quality of health, it is fair to say that the gains from Western medicine have peaked. If this is the case, what can we learn from other forms of medicine that have traditionally been practised around the world?

Let us introspect first, and try to understand the various benefits that come from medical treatment.

Step 1: You go see a doctor who has typically spent at least the better part of a decade studying the human body and its various afflictions.

Benefit: You are already starting to feel better at this point because you have taken the initiative to seek help.

Step 2: The doctor listens to you.

Benefit: Someone highly qualified has given you their shoulder to cry on, however briefly.

Step 3: The doctor charges you a fee.

Benefit: Since you paid for the visit, your mind delegates the problem to the doctor and makes you feel better. It is well known that we value the things we pay for, and the value is closely linked to the cost.

Step 4: The doctor gives you a prescription for some pills.

Benefit: Even if the pills are only sugar pills, you feel better because the placebo effect is an incredibly powerful curing agent.

Benefit: In Western medicine (unlike, say, homeopathy) these prescription pills have gone through extensive clinical trials and have proven their effectiveness over and above the placebo effect, so they do have an additional value (which is typically countered to some extent by side effects).

Step 5: The doctor thinks there is a larger problem, and refers you to a specialist.

Benefit: This is pretty much the domain of Western medicine. A specialist referral will greatly increase your cost of treatment, but those who can afford it will get the best that conventional medicine has to offer, be it surgery or extensive steps to isolate the health problem and treat it.

Step 6: You feel better in a few days.

Benefit: With time, most common illnesses go away even when you don't use medication. This is because the human body is capable of healing itself in most cases.

As stated above, there are multiple steps while interacting with a doctor. Of these steps, Western medicine has truly come into its own in Steps 4 and 5, and this is where it is a step above other forms of medicine.

But looking at the multiple stages in this treatment process, the effectiveness of each of those stages depends on :

1. The amount of time the doctor gives you.
2. The cost.
3. Your belief in the doctor's curing powers.
4. Whether the medicine treats the symptoms.
5. How good your overall symbiote and immune balance is to begin with.

Now here is the interesting part. The main difference between the various established forms of medicine that are practised in the world today is whether the medicine actually treats the symptoms. While Western medicine uses the scientific method explicitly to create medicines that can treat symptoms, other forms of medicine such as Ayurveda or Chinese medicine do not concern themselves with treating symptoms. Instead, they try to restore the overall health balance in the body, thus allowing the symptoms to resolve themselves.

I am a strong believer in the concept of health balance, where all the factors that contribute to positive health are in a state of balance. We have to accept that there is no shortcut or easy solution in the form of a pill or single treatment that transfers responsibility for your health from you to someone else.

The reality is that good health is one step below the surface. It's a bit like playing chess. When my seven-year-old nephew challenged me to a game of chess, I was delighted to sit down with him. One of the most amazing things about children is how they telegraph their thoughts through facial expressions. I could see exactly what he was thinking, and simply by following his eyes as they moved around the chessboard, I could see what he was going to do next. He had just learnt a new chess trick, and merrily oblivious to my three decades of chess experience, was getting ready to defeat me in just four moves. Needless to say, it was wonderful to see the look on his face when he checkmated me and won!

Chess is a game of pure strategy, where every move you make has increasingly stronger consequences on later moves, and ultimately on whether you win or lose. When children are first taught chess, they tend simply to look at each move as an individual step; they don't think ahead to what the consequences of the move might be in the next two or three steps. Experienced players think two or three steps ahead, giving them a strong advantage over a beginner. Quite often in chess, a step that seems at first glance to be mediocre or even bad turns out to provide an advantage that wins the game for the experienced player.

Good health is similar to this. When you are sick,

your initial thought is always to make the symptoms go away, rather than treat the underlying cause of the illness. Unfortunately, modern medicine is geared to this instant gratification process. This is wrong, as the body itself is like a chess board, with your immune system and symbiote on one team and pathogenic strains of bacteria and viruses on the other. The symptoms you see during an illness are caused mostly by your own immune system reacting to an invader. Looking at it this way, we can see that treating just the symptoms with medicine can make the disease last longer because the medicine does not actually fight the disease; it simply fights our immune system, which is already working hard on our behalf.

Fevers are a good example. A fever is simply the immune system's way of raising the body temperature so that pathogens are literally burned to death. Unless the fever is extremely high, treating it with aspirin can actually prolong the illness!

Another example is the link between chronic bacterial infections and anaemia, which is a disease caused by a lack of iron in the body. People with anaemia show signs of fatigue because iron plays a very important role in transporting energy to our body's cells. Iron is an essential mineral that binds with the haemoglobin in red blood cells and helps to carry oxygen from the lungs to every cell in the body. Anaemic people have cells that are literally starved for oxygen, causing low energy levels and fatigue.

People with chronic tuberculosis infections are also often anaemic. As we shall see in more detail in later chapters, many bacteria in the human body need iron to grow. In people with tuberculosis, anaemia is caused by the immune system deliberately lowering iron levels, in order to starve the tuberculosis bacteria. 'Treating' this anaemia with iron supplements will make the tuberculosis infection much worse.[2]

There is another huge problem in modern medicine, and this is the economic incentive for treating diseases; there is no financial incentive for doctors to focus on preventive medicine, because that would simply reduce the number of their patients (and their income). The incentives are in fact the opposite because doctors are paid per visit. This means that even though most doctors are truly driven by a sense of compassion and duty to cure their patients, the incentives in the business of general medicine favour a situation in which patients have long-term chronic conditions that demand frequent visits to treat the symptoms, because this is how doctors in Western medicine are paid.

For example, a patient with a chronic illness like diabetes provides a long-term income stream to doctors. She will need regular visits to put her on a sugar management diet, and progressively more care as diabetes ravages her body over the course of the next twenty, even thirty years. Think of this: one out of three people who are alive today will develop diabetes! This number was less in earlier generations, and we need to really question whether a health management system where doctors benefit simply from managing chronic illnesses is the right approach. Has it contributed to the epidemic of diabetes and other chronic illnesses that we see today?

The key question for modern medicine is this: how do we align financial incentives for doctors so that they actually benefit from patient health and from promoting preventive medicine?

In China, until a hundred years ago, doctors were paid for exactly the opposite of the modern financial incentive model. In other words, you employed your local village doctor on a monthly retainer, and paid him for every month that you are healthy. If you fell sick during a month, you didn't have to pay your doctor, as he had failed to keep you healthy. It is easy to see how the doctor would then have a strong incentive not only to keep you healthy but also to cure you as quickly as possible.

Interestingly, we may be returning to some form of this practice, at least in the USA, where a new concept known as 'concierge care' is rapidly growing.[3] This is a system that is still undergoing innovation and there are a lot of problems to iron out, but if preventive medicine becomes the main focus of concierge care, there is reason to be optimistic.

Until there is a public health system that focuses on preventive care, we must take care of our own health. The basic premise of this book is that good health, like skill at chess, is based on our ability to think beyond the first step of just treating symptoms. Once we focus on trying to understand and treat the root causes of illness, we will end up with better outcomes. This is exactly where understanding the human symbiote can help.

The human symbiote is basically the trillions of bacteria that live on our body and in our gut, a living ecosystem that we carry with us everywhere we go. A proper balance of this symbiote is essential for good health, and we will also see how changes in the composition of the symbiote are an important signal for diseases in the underlying human body.

Remember also that a multiple-step process like good health can take time. Do not expect immediate results from the prescriptions in this book. If your symbiote is off-balance or weak, strengthening it or restoring the balance can take time, and sometimes it involves a process of trial and error. Patience is key to improving health, and we should learn to temper our expectations of taking a pill to restore health. People don't generally lose their health overnight, so they cannot gain it back overnight either. Even if the symptoms of ill-health appear suddenly, it usually is the end result of a long period of time, during which the underlying disease develops silently.

In the coming chapters, I will try and give you some answers to common health problems. So let us begin, and get to know our dearest and closest friend, our symbiote.

1

KNOWING YOUR BACTERIAL FRIENDS

Every inch of the planet's surface is covered with bacteria, from the top of Mount Everest to the bottom of the Mariana Trench in the Pacific Ocean. It was once thought that large parts of the open ocean surface were free of bacteria, but scientists know better now. With the development of DNA sequencing techniques in the last five to ten years, we know that bacteria are everywhere. Until some years ago, the polar regions of our planet were considered to be barren, but it turns out that they may contain the world's most bio-diverse soils in terms of microbes. There are subterranean bacteria deep inside our planet that get their energy directly from the earth's crust, without even indirect solar energy playing a part. Bacteria have been found in highly inhospitable conditions of temperature and pressure, so we have to assume that much of the earth's core also contains bacteria, except maybe at very extreme temperatures and pressures. So it is not surprising that scientists wonder if there is bacterial life on other planets and moons as well, wherever there is access to a continuous energy source.

There is a respectable theory that life on earth itself may have begun through colonization by bacteria riding in on an asteroid. New research shows that bacteria make up a majority of the biomass on our planet. It was once thought that bacteria are so tiny that while they may be numerous, they do not comprise a big portion of the biomass, but research by the late Stephen Jay Gould[1] at Harvard University, as well as by others, shows that given the number of bacteria not only on the planet but deep inside its surface, they are likely to add up to a majority of the planetary biomass, even more than trees.

It is not hard to see that human life on this planet without bacteria is neither possible nor desirable. Bacteria serve essential purposes from sewage treatment to decomposition of organic matter. Bacteria have been used to clean up oil spills, like the huge Macondo spill in the Gulf of Mexico. In medicine, bacteria are used to make insulin, growth factors and antibodies. The very gasoline we use to fuel our cars was made by the bacterial decomposition of plant and animal matter over millions of years. Bacteria have co-evolved with the human species, so much so that they are not merely passengers on the human evolutionary timeline but partners and even co-drivers. We know from evolutionary studies that microbes have shaped the course of human evolution. What is really surprising is how long it took modern science to figure out their role in the survival of the human species and in improving our quality of life. Until very recently, the most basic medicine in the toolkit of Western doctors has been the antibiotic. Science and medicine have treated bacteria as enemies to be tamed and destroyed, with terrible consequences for public health that are only now becoming apparent.

Given the intimate partnership between microbes and the human species, the only question is whether the bacteria-dominated ecosystem that coexists on the human body is in sync with our overall health. Destroying or altering this bacterial ecosystem balance is a very bad idea, since the ecosystem that replaces it may not be as beneficial to us, and could quite easily be harmful if it is not compatible with our body. Equally, we cannot meet our desire for better health without improving the quality and compatibility of the symbiote with our body.

Let's try and understand the body from the symbiote's perspective. As far as the symbiote is concerned, the human body is the host. There are good hosts and there are bad hosts. The symbiote is a complete living ecosystem. It is also an evolutionary machine, meaning that for the most part it is continually adapting to its host's environment and evolving, with the main aim being its own survival. The symbiote is on an evolutionary voyage, and our body is the vessel.

It is important to understand one thing: if the symbiote had self-awareness in the same way our body does, it would view the human body as a host that provides it with nutrients, and for the most part a safe place to conduct its business of evolution and adaptation. It would probably liken the behaviour of its host to that of a capricious god. This god seems to provide the symbiote with everything, yet it is prone to doing odd things like bathing (bad for skin symbiote), going out in cold weather without a sweater (adds stress to the symbiote balance) or taking antibiotics (really awful for the whole symbiote).

The symbiote of a healthy eater is very different from that of someone who lives on junk food. The human host provides not only calories to the symbiote but also micro- and macro-nutrients, and the symbiote evolves in response. At the same time, the symbiote bacteria themselves produce both beneficial and toxic by-products, which in turn have a significant effect on the human host.

Let us look at what happens when we eat red meat. Red meat is very nutritious and energy rich, but it has some harmful side effects. As the meat is digested in our large intestine by the gut symbiote, it produces harmful molecules known as free radicals. This is the symbiote's fault, but it is a by-product of the red meat digestion process. Free radicals are implicated in everything from cancer to heart disease, so doctors recommend reducing the intake of red meat. But is there another solution that can stop the production of free radicals during the digestive process, one that does not involve all of us turning vegetarian? It turns out there is—red wine!

Scientists have long found that drinking a glass of red wine daily seems to be highly beneficial, and the so-called nutraceutical industry has zeroed in on an antioxidant called resveratrol that is found in red wine. Studies show that fruit flies pumped with resveratrol live significantly longer than regular fruit flies, and now resveratrol is available in pill form at a store near you!

But wait, things are not as clear cut as they seem. First of all, a glass of red wine does not have a whole lot of resveratrol, and of this amount only a tiny bit is absorbed into the blood stream. Taking high doses of pure resveratrol in pill form is also useless. Resveratrol in pill form is not what scientists refer to as 'bioavailable', meaning that it is not in a form that can be absorbed by the body. So how do we explain the fact that the benefits of drinking red wine seem to far outweigh the impact of the small dose of resveratrol that gets into the blood stream?

The key to this mystery is simple: the effect of red wine on red meat is mechanical, and very easy to explain. According to new research, if you drink a glass of red wine along with red meat, the free radicals produced by the gut symbiote during the breakdown of red meat are immediately neutralized by the resveratrol in the red wine, so the stomach plays the role of a 'bioreactor'.[2] All this happens before any nutrients are absorbed into the blood stream. This presents an elegant and delightful solution to improve health in red meat eaters: whenever you eat red meat, drink a glass of red wine (or have green tea if you are a teetotaller).

This research also suggests that if you are not a red meat eater, a glass of red wine will have little or no impact on your health, as far as its resveratrol content is concerned, although there are benefits from the moderate alcohol content of the wine itself. But since red wine is largely drunk in countries where people also eat lots of red meat, it is hard to separate the benefits of the combination from the benefit of red wine alone. Later we will talk about the beneficial effects of moderate alcohol consumption, whether it is beer or wine or spirits.

The concept of bioreactors applies not only to the stomach but also to cooking food. For instance, when grilling meat, harmful compounds called heterocyclic amines are released. These amines are linked to certain types of cancer in humans. These amines are countered by the herb rosemary, which contains powerful antioxidants called rosmarinic acid and carnosol. A recent study showed that adding rosemary to meat before grilling or barbecuing reduces heterocyclic amines by over 90 per cent.[3] The next time you have grilled lamb with rosemary, think not only of the great flavour but also of good health!

These bioreactions happen all the time in the cooking process. Marinating meat also reduces the production of harmful compounds during cooking, particularly when the marinades contain garlic or onion. With cookery shows becoming so prevalent on television these days, it is only a matter of time before television chefs incorporate these healthy combinations explicitly into their shows.

The First Line of Defence

Think of bacteria as your first line of immunity and defence against pathogens attacking your body. A pathogen attempting to take hold in your body must deal first with the fact that every inch of your body has already been colonized by tens of billions of bacteria that have evolved specifically to live on and in your body. When they see an intruder, a battle to compete for resources and even physical space ensues to drive it out. It is only when external pathogens beat the first line of bacterial defence and take hold in your body that the body's immune system begins to respond. The helpful intruder-fighting bacteria that live on your body are nominally called commensal bacteria, meaning that while the bacteria benefit from their relationship with the human host, the human host derives neither a benefit nor bears any cost.

John Milton in his sonnet 'On His Blindness' said it best:

. . . God doth not need
Either man's work or his own gifts: who best
Bear his mild yoke, they serve him best [. . .]
They also serve who only stand and wait.

The last line of this poem captures the role of every bacterium that lives on and in our body. Bacteria are the first line of defence in health, and scientists are now beginning to understand that there is no such thing as commensal or neutral bacteria when it comes to our symbiote. The very fact that the so-called commensal bacteria's existence is stopping pathogens from taking hold in the human body means that they provide a real benefit to us and should therefore be called symbiotic bacteria instead of commensal bacteria. Indeed, every bacterial species that lives on and in our bodies has a purpose, with apologies to Milton!

These symbiotic bacteria are everywhere: on your skin, in your nose, inside the gut and bowels, and in your mouth. We will discuss the role of all these and more in the coming chapters, but let us start with the skin, the largest organ in the human body.

The skin is full of bacteria. Between your elbow and your forearm, there are some 140 species, and the estimates of bacterial species on your entire body are in the thousands, with more species being identified all the time. These bacteria live on a steady diet of dead skin cells and sweat. In fact, the role of sweat is very important for the health of the skin symbiote and the skin itself.

There is a new hypothesis that our sweat glands are the key to regulating the skin symbiote. When we sweat, we release small quantities of a nitrogen-based compound called ammonia, which encourages a group of ammonia-oxidizing bacteria to live on our skin.[4] These bacteria are totally harmless because they can only digest the ammonia released in the sweat. Nitrates are by-products of digesting this ammonia. In turn, these nitrates act as a kind of natural disinfectant, since most pathogenic bacteria cannot survive in a nitrate environment. Seen from this perspective, the role of sweating in human health becomes clearer. Next time you head to the gym, rest assured that the sweat you work up is good for you and for your symbiote as well!

The Disinfectant Industry and the Huge Damage It Causes Public Health

Never underestimate the power of marketing, and always keep in mind that most businesses are out to sell you something, and their priority is mostly to sell their stuff, not to look after your well-being. The range of selfishness in the business world can be put on a scale of one to ten, one being fairly altruistic and ten being, say, extreme greed. Most businesses probably fall between five and ten, meaning they offer some value and well-being along with their primary aim of making money.

For instance, I would rank the newspaper industry about five on this scale. The financial goal of newspaper publishers is to sell newspapers, although undoubtedly newspaper editors also try to report news objectively. This tends to create a compromise situation where news coverage on stories is simply slanted with the view of selling maximum copy. So the reporting is mostly genuine, but it is sometimes sensationalized to maximize sales.

But sensationalism is not limited to newspapers. Entire industries are built on sensationalist drivel. The bottled water industry is a prime example, convincing us that somehow their product is superior to the cheap tap water equivalent, despite scientific evidence to the contrary. At the same time, I would not begrudge the bottled water industry their right to sell their products, because all said and done they do no harm to public health. There is, however, a significant environmental cost to their existence and governments should make them pay the full share of the cost through the taxation system.

On the other hand, the entire household disinfectants industry is a danger to human health, and easily busts through my ten-point scale in terms of the sheer greed-based misinformation that they spread. Basically, the whole industry is a combination of junk science and sensationalism that preys on your irrational fear of germs.

Just look at the word 'disinfect', which is a term that only a marketing genius could have thought of. It is the opposite of infect, a word that in our minds evokes a notion that some bad bugs have taken over a surface in our home or body, and are threatening to wage war against us. In a single word, 'disinfectant' not only puts fear into our minds that we are under attack, but also offers a solution in a bottle that will repel invaders. Brilliant!

There are several problems with this approach. The first is that the common bacteria found on surfaces in the home and on the body are perfectly safe and harmless. They do not need to be repelled or interfered with.

The second problem is that even if for some reason you insist on killing billions of harmless bacteria, disinfectants are temporarily effective at best. The bacteria are back within minutes or even seconds. Using disinfectant is the household equivalent of trying to empty the Atlantic Ocean with a bucket!

The third problem is that the process of trying to kill bacteria will actually eliminate the weakest strains while allowing stronger and more resistant bacteria to survive and grow. So, you will eventually end up with hardier and more resistant bacteria, which makes the whole exercise pointless, doesn't it?

The fourth issue relates to what can happen if you use disinfectant on your hands. You simply wipe out entire colonies of bacteria, for a few seconds anyway. You then pick up a fresh colony of bacteria from the next surface you touch, whether it is your own body, your clothes or a counter top.

When this happens, there is a small but significant risk that the new colonizers of the disinfected hand may not be your own skin flora but a hardy new arrival from outside. If this happens, the whole point of using disinfectant on the hands becomes counterproductive, particularly if the new arrival turns out to be a pathogenic strain.

But what about viruses, especially the common cold virus, you might ask. Don't disinfectants kill viruses? The answer is yes, they do, but there are much better ways to control the spread of the common cold virus. We pick up the common cold virus from infected surfaces, which are likely to be the most common surfaces that people come in contact with. The best examples of these are lift buttons, door handles in public spaces, public phones, supermarket checkout pens and ATM machines. None of these has to do with your home, which in comparison is an exceptionally safe zone. I have never seen anyone carry around disinfectant and meticulously use it on every public contact surface before they touch it, but such people may well exist in our crazy world!

But what about using hand sanitizer every few minutes, to keep your hands clean from viruses? Let me answer this in two ways.

First, the fact is that we are infected with several cold viruses most of the time without any symptoms showing. It is worth noting here that when we catch a cold, with runny nose and sore throat and fever, it is not the virus we are feeling, but our own immune system's response to the virus.

In most cases, cold viruses do not elicit this massive immune response from the body's defences. This is because viruses use us like a bed-and-breakfast; they stay for a while, long enough to replicate and spread to the next host, and our body's immune system quietly evicts them without a fuss. If you try to disrupt this process, it is likely to be futile because viruses are everywhere. In fact, it could well be counter-productive. If you keep trying to avoid viruses, you may have fewer colds, but the ones you do have will end up being more severe, because the immune system gets used to a low virus environment. An immune system that is not used to a constant barrage of viruses is likely to attack the cold viruses that do get into your nose with a big immune response with lots of nasty symptoms.

Second, I do agree that when there is a particularly nasty strain of virus going around, bird flu, for instance, it is well worth avoiding it. However, there is a very effective sanitizer that can get rid of viruses that you pick up on your hands during the flu season. This sanitizer is called soap and water.

Yes, the best disinfectant for your hands is soap and water, and it is the mechanical action of rubbing together soaped-up hands that washes away germs, particularly viruses. While it is definitely prudent to wash your hands regularly to avoid viruses during flu season, there is never a need outside of a hospital environment to use disinfectants or sanitizers of any kind.

What about your kitchen surfaces at home, your dishes and even your toilets? A number of non-toxic alternatives are available, which clean very well without attempting to sterilize or 'disinfect'. These include baking soda, unscented liquid soap, lemon juice, white vinegar and washing soda.

A word on disinfectant soap in the bath or shower: avoid it like the plague. Just remind yourself that the point of bathing is to reduce the dirt on your body and to wash away any stray viruses that may have hitched a ride on you. The point is absolutely not to try and disinfect your body. Remember that the skin symbiote is a living ecosystem of bacteria that is benign and well-suited to your body, and it is the first line of defence against pathogenic bacteria. If you continuously assault it with disinfectant, you could eventually end up with a pathogenic strain that dominates your skin symbiote, and could actually harm you.

There is another big reason to avoid disinfectants or an overly sterile environment: the increased risk of developing allergies, which we will discuss in detail later.

Public Sanitation Can Be a Load of Bullshit

You might be wondering what on earth this section is all about. In fact, I am talking about bullshit in the very literal sense, as in cow excrement. In villages across India, China and Africa, millions of people use cow or buffalo excrement mixed with water as a floor and wall sanitizer. Visitors to

India see lots of cows and buffaloes, but few have wondered why there is hardly any cow excrement to be found on the streets. It's because cow dung is a prized commodity; someone will come along and quickly grab any cow pies that are found on the roads. A lot of it is used to make dried cow cakes that can be burned for fuel. But a significant amount is mixed with water, and painted on the floors and walls of the homes of villagers and the urban poor.

Now why on earth would so many people do that? The answer is that cow dung is a natural sanitizer. Cow pies are a rich source of what are known as commensal bacteria, primarily E. coli, which are bacteria that for the most part are completely harmless to humans, and help fight off pathogens that may otherwise colonize floor surfaces. In fact, there are over a hundred known strains of E. coli, and many of them are not only part of the human symbiote, but also produce vitamin K in our bodies. However, E. coli has a terrible reputation in the West because there is one particular pathogenic strain, O157:H7, that causes serious infections in humans. But it is worth reiterating that most strains of E. coli are not only completely harmless to humans, they are beneficial to us.

People who live in dung-sanitized homes have no allergies, few bacterial infections, and despite their poverty, are quite healthy in countries where tropical diseases are common.

Now I am not suggesting that we all ring our local farm

for some cow pies and dab it on our home surfaces! But these villagers have the right idea about what constitutes proper sanitization. It is an abundance of friendly bacteria around the house and on our bodies that helps keep our immune systems healthy and wards off pathogenic strains. We can certainly get there without smelling of cow dung, but it does require us to remove 'disinfectants' from our homes and lives.

Symbiote and the Common Cold

Let's face it, most of the everyday illnesses that we are bound to face in our lives are related to the common cold. While it is fascinating to read about exotic illnesses like Ebola, it is, in fact, the common cold caused by one of over a hundred types of rhinoviruses that we encounter the most in our lives. The common cold cannot altogether be avoided, but there are simple steps we can take that decrease the incidence of the symptoms and their severity. Let us look at the most basic step, which is to stay warm in cold weather.

What your grandmother said about wearing warm clothes when going out in the cold is true. Your odds of getting sick rise dramatically when you go from a hot to a cold environment. The simple reason for this is that a lot of symbiote bacteria in your nasal cavity and in the mucous membranes of your eyes do not like the cold, and they die when the temperature drops. Viruses, on the other hand, seem to thrive in cold weather, so coupled with a compromised symbiote, you are giving cold viruses a free pass to infect your nasal cavities if you dress improperly in cold weather.

Science has gone back and forth on this one. The very name 'catching a cold' comes from observed fact through the ages; if you go out in the cold you will get sick. But when viruses were discovered as the cause of the common cold, science turned its back on the importance of ambient temperature, especially change in ambient temperature, which is a leading catalyst in cold infections. Scientists recently conducted experiments on students, subjecting them to artificially cool conditions to see if it had any impact on them developing illnesses. The result is what my mother-in-law has always been saying, that there is a strong causal link between being out in cold weather and catching a cold.[5]

There are several theories about why this is the case, but let us look at a compelling one. It is well known that hundreds of species of viruses can cause the common cold. It is also known that most of the colds that humans catch are asymptomatic, which is to say that we may have a cold but nine out of ten times we show no symptoms. A runny nose, fever, headache, are all caused by the immune system's response to the cold virus, not by the cold virus itself.

It is therefore reasonable conjecture that the reason most colds show no symptoms is that the symbiote barrier is fighting off most colds with minimal immune system backup, so we do not see the external expressions of the cold.

But when we go through a rapid lowering in ambient temperature, either the cold virus that is infecting us at that particular time becomes more potent, or our defences are somehow weakened. Since we know that viruses like the cold and bacteria do not, some combination of both these possibilities is likely. When a weakened symbiote meets a stronger viral adversary, the immune system is forced into a general response, which gives rise to all the nasty symptoms. Another possibility is that the immune system treats cold weather as a form of stress and powers down, thereby increasing the body's vulnerability to viruses. Stress, as scientists know, is a well-known immune suppressant.

It is also true that people who live with a high amount of stress are prone to more illnesses, including more colds. The reasons for this are not well understood, but there are two primary chemicals that are secreted by the body when under stress—adrenalin and cortisol. These chemicals are very useful in increasing energy levels and marshalling a general immune response, but they come at a cost: there is a 'downtime' after the stress response is finished, when the immune system powers down in order to recover. This downtime is similar to what happens when we go out in the cold.

Both these routes provide a foothold for viruses, which then have to be fought off with an immune response that manifests in cold symptoms.

But stress is a constant in our life. It is not possible to get rid of it, because as we do more and more to minimize the causes of stress in our lives, our perspective narrows, and we are stressed by ever smaller issues.

The solution for most of us is not to run away from stress, but to face it head on and learn to manage it effectively, and look after our body, diet and fitness levels as well as we can.

Antibiotic Misuse

Paul has a cold. At the first sign of a runny nose he runs to the clinic and insists his doctor write him an antibiotic prescription. The doctor obliges and prescribes a one-week course. Paul feels better after taking the antibiotics for three days and stops taking the medicine.

There are at least three huge problems in this story, which unfortunately takes place thousands of times a day all over the world. The first point is that the symptoms of the common cold are caused by the body's reaction to a viral infection, and antibiotics have no effect on viruses. The prescription was therefore unnecessary and ineffective; Paul would have felt better after three days anyway, whether he had taken the medicine or not. Not only are the antibiotics ineffective, but Paul has also quite possibly wiped out a good portion of his symbiote, thereby upsetting his natural symbiote balance and setting in motion a string of diseases that he will face in a few weeks or months, long after he has forgotten about the cold and how he had 'treated' it.

Of course, in many cases, the symbiote balance is simply restored once the antibiotics course is complete, but this is not always the case. Paul could easily end up with strains of bacteria different from what his body is used to, and some of these could even be pathogenic. At the very least, he has taken a significant and unnecessary risk to his health, merely because of the placebo effect of taking some pills for his common cold.

The next problem is that Paul stopped the antibiotic course halfway through after feeling better. A lot of people make this mistake. Chances are that there might be a strain of bacteria in his symbiote that has pathogenic capabilities, which has now been strengthened because Paul stopped the course midway and did not wipe out this pathogenic strain. Given that millions of Pauls are prescribed antibiotics every year and the trillions of bacterial cells each of these people individually harbours, it is most certain that pathogens will evolve antibiotic resistance when repeatedly exposed to antibiotics, and it is also a certainty that resistant strains will then multiply, making the antibiotic obsolete over time. This is a lesson that modern medicine has learned the hard way.

The US Surgeon General is said to have declared in 1962 that with the advent of antibiotics 'the book of infectious diseases can now be ultimately closed', implying that we have won the war on infectious diseases. This sentiment was widely held for the next twenty years, until the emergence of HIV and the resurgence of antibiotic-resistant strains of pathogenic bacteria created another health crisis, one that continues to this day.

According to the American Centers for Disease Control (CDC), 5 per cent of patients admitted to hospitals acquire an infectious disease while at the hospital.[6] If it is a long-term managed care facility, the number is about 10 per cent. The mortality rate for these is quite high; estimates state that between 30,000–70,000 people in the US die every year of an infection they acquired while they were at the hospital being treated for something else. It is a large number comparable to the annual highway traffic deaths in the US (40,000). Moreover, it should be preventable, as hospitals are supposed to be clean and sterile places where people go to get better. In fact, it turns out that hospital-acquired infections are particularly dangerous, because of two reasons. One is that hospital patients are more prone to infections than other people. But the second reason is more important: bacterial strains that can survive in the hostile, sterile and antibiotic-laden environs of the hospital evolve into some very hardy pathogens, capable of developing resistance to the most powerful antibiotics that modern medicine has in its arsenal today.

In fact, modern medicine has actually created these superbugs. In the fight against infectious diseases, antibiotics are of course a potent and necessary weapon. But it is the misuse of antibiotics, using them where they are unnecessary or inappropriate, that has really driven antibiotic resistance.

But the story does not stop here; in fact, it is just beginning. The indiscriminate use of antibiotics has led to a crisis in public health of epidemic proportions, and now we have created powerful lobbies that have a vested interest in creating ever stronger antibiotics to fight the ever more powerful superbugs.

It is time to get off this escalator and consider a new approach to managing bacteria. In the meantime, let us look at how antibiotic misuse has likely led to an extraordinary epidemic of obesity in the Western world.

Stomach Ulcers and a 'Nuclear Response'

Helicobacterpylori is a bacterium that lives in the stomachs of over 70 per cent of the world's population. It has co-evolved with humans, and has existed in our stomachs throughout our evolutionary history. It is a hardy bacterium, which is not surprising since the stomach is a highly acidic environment, and you have to be quite a strong customer to survive in there.

H. pylori has a very important function in the human symbiote. This species belongs to a family of bacteria called firmicutes, and science is only now discovering that firmicutes have a massive role to play in obesity among humans. When H. pylori is wiped out, other firmicutes not only take its place but actually dominate the stomach, reducing the ratio of another type of stomach bacteria called bacteroidetes. An excess of firmicutes leads to obesity because firmicutes encourage the body to lay down excess stores of fat in the body. This fat accumulates everywhere, particularly around the abdomen, which causes the classic pear-shaped body common in middle-aged men in the Western world.

But there is an astonishing truth about H. pylori, a truth that caused modern medicine to declare war on it and try to wipe it from the human symbiote despite our lack of proper understanding of the role it plays in our health.

Once upon a time there was a disease called chronic stomach ulcers. For sufferers, it was a debilitating illness, causing pain and bleeding in the stomach. No one could figure out the cause of these ulcers. Some thought it was viral, but they could not identify the virus. There was no cure either, and the prescription was a long-term course of antacids or stomach acid inhibitors, which merely treated the symptoms.

Then, in 1982, everything changed. Two Australian doctors discovered that ulcers were actually caused by a strain of bacteria called H. pylori, which is a normal resident in people's stomachs. The duo won the Nobel Prize for medicine in 2005 for their discovery, and now ulcer treatment involves a course of several medicines, including antibiotics, to rid the body of H. pylori. Everyone lived happily ever after, right? Wrong!

The first point is that not every strain of H. pylori causes ulcers, only certain strains do, and there is a huge variation in strains of this bacterium. There is a very basic rule when it comes to bacteria, including H. pylori. Bacteria that are able to jump quickly from host to host are in general more harmful to the host, and bacteria that have a tough time moving from host to host are more beneficial.

In the case of H. pylori, studies show that strains that are more motile are more likely to cause ulcers.[7] This makes sense, because producing a toxin, such as the one that causes ulcers, imposes a metabolic cost on the bacterium. In evolutionary terms, what it means is that if the toxic strain was not able to move quickly from host to host, it would reproductively be outcompeted and outnumbered by other strains of the same bacterium.

Whatever the cause of the misbehaviour of certain strains of H. pylori, the reaction of modern medicine was predictable. With the help of the pharmaceutical industry, health authorities wiped out H. pylori in the West through antibiotics. Earlier, 90 per cent Americans had H. pylori in their stomachs, and now only 10 per cent do. So what? you may well ask. Good riddance to a pathogenic strain, even if other H. pylori strains are benign! But H. pylori is not merely benign, it has an enormous role to play in our health balance.

It appears that people with H. pylori in their stomachs are far less likely to be overweight. Given that obesity and its attendant problems are the single biggest health crisis facing the Western world, this important link with a stomach bacterium must be fully investigated. How exactly H. pylori keeps body weight in check is still being debated, but there are two schools of thought.

The first says that H. pylori regulates a hormone called ghrelin, a chemical that signals to the brain when the stomach is empty. In the absence of H. pylori, levels of ghrelin increase, causing people to overeat. You can blame fastfood and super-sizing all you want, but the fastfood industry was merely responding to the demands of consumers, who in turn were responding to their brains being unable to tell them when to stop eating! So, who is to blame?

The second school looks at the composition of gut bacteria in lean versus obese people. Most gut bacteria belong to two categories: firmicutes (H. pylori and friends) and bacteroidetes. It turns out that obese people have a higher proportion of firmicutes than bacteroidetes. These firmicutes are not only more efficient in digesting food for absorption by the body, they also suppress chemicals that the body produces to reduce the amount of fat that is stored, thereby prompting the body to store more fat. In other words, some firmicutes adapt to guide the body to become obese, and these are the ones that take root when H. pylori is eliminated.

Both schools of thought could be right, but whichever wins out in the end, it is certainly true that widespread use of antibiotics has a) greatly reduced H. pylori in Western stomachs, and b) has coincided with a ghastly epidemic of obesity in the West.

If obesity is an illness caused by the overuse of antibiotics, then the consequences of obesity also manifest in an array of autoimmune diseases. Consider Type 2 diabetes. This is an illness primarily affecting the obese, whereby they develop resistance to insulin, a hormone produced in the pancreas that helps human cells absorb blood sugar and turn it into energy. There is evidence that this resistance is the result of the immune system's response to excess body fat. This excess fat is full of cancer-causing compounds called free radicals. To fight this continuous rain of free radicals produced by the excess fat, the body sends out a tumour-suppressing protein, which in turn causes a chronic inflammatory response that takes the form of insulin resistance.[8]

Linking the explosion of obesity in the West in the last two decades to antibiotic misuse has wide-ranging implications. It means that the obesity epidemic is not behavioural but physiological, that too because of a symbiote imbalance. It also means that the vast array of diseases caused by obesity can be reversed, by getting to the root (or in this case, gut!) cause.

Science is now beginning to see H. pylori as the immune system's 'boot camp drill-sergeant', a symbiotic organism that helps its human host in a wide variety of ways. A recent study shows that the presence of H. pylori in the stomach is linked to lower rates of childhood asthma.[9] This link could work in one of two ways. The first possibility is that H. pylori is directly responsible for desensitizing the immune system so that it does not react against benign proteins. The second is that it is likely that H. pylori colonization is a general indicator of how the human host deals with the symbiote; people who declare war on H. pylori are also the same folks who have a misguided sense of hygiene, and who are trying to eliminate all microbes from their environs, causing the immune system to go mad!

2

DIET, BATHROOM HABITS
AND THE SYMBIOTE

❦

Suzy and her husband were giddy with excitement; they had just brought their newborn baby home from hospital. Looking at the tiny, fragile person, Suzy was overcome with a feeling of protectiveness. She had already cleaned the house until it was spotless. But Suzy saw germs everywhere. No one was allowed to touch the baby until they had washed their hands with soap and water, dried them on disposable napkins and applied alcohol-based disinfectant. Suzy herself was extremely careful with the baby, sterilizing the bottles and nipples before bottlefeeding the baby. The baby was doing very well. And then suddenly, when she was twenty days old, she started becoming restless and fussy, especially in the late evenings. Weeks of sleepless nights later, Suzy booked an appointment with the pediatrician.

He diagnosed the baby with colic, and explained that there was no cure and that the baby would be fine after three months or so. At her wit's end, Suzy went to a natural cure therapist, who advised Suzy to spit in the baby's mouth. Suzy was horrified and disgusted, but after three more sleepless nights she finally relented and fed the baby a tablespoon of her saliva. The colic disappeared overnight.

A hundred years after the discovery of antibiotics, science has come full circle and begun to realize the importance of bacteria in good health. When babies are born, they have no gut bacteria. They acquire their gut flora from their mothers, most likely through kisses. This essential process occurs in the first two weeks after birth, and it is around day twenty that the gut flora becomes essential for the baby's smooth digestion of milk. If this natural process of transferring gut flora does not take place, in this case because Suzy kept her baby's environment too sterile, it leads to colic. It has taken decades to figure out how to cure this common infant ailment, but no infant needs to suffer from this unnecessary discomfort ever again.

The human gut has thousands of different species of bacteria. In fact, a staggering 90 per cent of the bacteria that are part of the human symbiote live in the gut, mainly in the large intestine. Many foods, carbohydrates being the most essential among them, can only be digested by humans if gut flora is present. There is a significant scientific consensus to treat gut bacteria as a 'forgotten organ', given its importance in nutrition and good health. But for the purposes of this book, I refer to the entire symbiote as one, which includes the bacteria on our skin, in our mouth and everywhere else in our body.

A second culprit in Suzy's case could also be the lack of breastfeeding. There is a major unresolved debate on the breast- versus bottlefeeding issue in the West. While it is clear that bottlefeeding is not seriously damaging to the baby, we should keep in mind that breast milk is not just about calorific nutrition (which infant formula can provide equally well), but also about other forms of nutrition such as immune globulins (which pass on antibodies from the mother to the child) and probiotics. We will discuss immune globulins later, but breast milk is an important source of probiotics, and it is a fact that bottlefed babies have very different gut bacteria from breastfed ones, with breastfed babies showing a much higher quantity of probiotic bifidobacteria in their gut.[1] Formula-fed babies have more enterococci in their gut, which do not offer probiotic properties.

The Heart of the Immune System Is the Gut

What do the Israel–Syria border, the India–Pakistan border, the China–Russia border and the human gut have in common? This is not a political question as such, but what I am getting at is that these are all points of potential conflict. The reason is that they all represent the line of control between two competing religions/civilizations/political systems/ecosystems.

The human gut is the front line where the body's immune system ends and our symbiote bacteria begin. Some 90 per cent of the bacteria in our body are present in the gut, encased by a membrane made up of the immune system's frontline troops, who are determined to react to any pathogenic bacterial strains with a vigorous response. Keeping the bacterial ecosystem in the gut in a stable symbiotic balance occupies most of the resources of the human immune system.

You Are What You Eat

Most of us have a diet that we follow, but where does it come from? If you are Japanese or Indian, chances are that rice is a big part of your diet, but if you are Irish, then potatoes are more likely to be your staple.

The human symbiote adjusted to digesting a variety of food, so much so that at any given level of income, people have very similar life expectancies no matter where they live and what their diet. This is remarkable, given how different diets can be, but it shows how important the symbiote is in facilitating absorption of essential nutrients and minerals from all manner of diet. But this book is not too concerned with life expectancy, which in any event is continuing to rise in the developed world. This book is more concerned with the quality of the life that we lead, which in turn depends on how healthy we remain until the last stages of life.

Yes, if you eat fibrous cereal every day, have a big breakfast and a salad for lunch, eat lots of fruits and vegetables and cut out red meat, and have oily fish with healthy sides for dinner, you have maximized your chance at a healthy life. But for many of us, this ideal diet is not the reality. So, what should we do?

Well, the good news is that deviating a couple of times a week from the ideal diet does not make much difference to the outcome of good health. In other words, a couple of nights of eating red meat a week won't kill you any faster, and you will have a more enjoyable life to boot!

A Swiss doctor named Paracelsus said in 1567, 'There are no poisons, only poisonous doses.' What he meant at the time is that in a sufficiently high dosage any chemical or substance is harmful. The same goes for red meat or even a bowl of spinach. (Spinach contains oxalic acid, which can be harmful, provided you eat over ten pounds of it in one sitting!). So by all means, live a little, eat whatever you fancy as long as it is in moderation, and be wary of excess!

As far as your gut symbiote is concerned, pretty much any edible substance goes, as long as it is consumed in moderation.

At the other end of the spectrum, where hype about supplements rules supreme, I would argue that the entire vitamin supplement industry is a bunch of bunkum, for three reasons. The first is that at least in the developed world, we get plenty of vitamins from our regular diet, and there is no shortage of vitamins or minerals in our diet. The second reason is that many vitamin supplements have an almost zero absorption rate, meaning that the gut symbiote simply passes the stuff out of the other end without metabolizing any of it. This is something the clean-living guru Dr Dean Ornish calls 'creating dark urine', meaning that all these vitamins do is colour your urine dark brown, as they pass through your system unabsorbed. The main reason vitamin company executives are not in jail is because we can't prove that their products cause actual harm, even the ones that get absorbed by the digestive system. You might as well eat a piece of chalk and save yourself some money.

The third reason why vitamin supplements are not necessary is even more interesting, because it has to do with our symbiote.

Symbiote Bacteria Are Vitamin Factories

It turns out that your symbiote bacteria make some of the essential vitamins that the human body needs.

Vitamin K is made by bacteria in the large intestine. Somewhere between a third and half the vitamin K that we need is produced in this way. Vitamin B12 cannot be made by plants or animals; only bacteria can synthesize it. A host of organisms in the human gut have the capability to make plenty of B12 for the body's needs. Vitamin B5 is also made in the gut and absorbed through the lining of the gut.[2]

Of course, some of these can be replaced by vitamin supplements. But what is the appropriate dose? We know that some vitamins, like vitamin A, can be damaging to the bones if taken in excess. And we know nothing about how the absorption dynamic in the body changes when you start taking those vitamin supplements that do get absorbed. For instance, if excess vitamins are ingested, it is only natural that the body reduces the absorption rate. Over time, the body even develops a kind of resistance to these excess vitamins. Then, if you forget to take your vitamins one day, you create a sudden shortage that the body might have trouble coping with. Why would you want to subject yourself to this artificial and unnecessary regime, when the alternative is to maintain a healthy symbiote and let it deal with it?

A story about vegetable gardening may be illustrative here. As even amateur gardeners know, the right amount of water and nutrients is critical to growing vegetables. One summer I was growing tomatoes in my London home, and I took religious care of them. But I had to go away for just two days when the plants were flowering, and I was not able to water them. The result was a total disaster, as the flowers dried up and fell and I was left with a row of tomato plants with no fruit. These days I have become smarter about my vegetables. I use a self-watering planter, which is basically a reservoir of water that sits under the plant pot. The roots of the plant grow into the reservoir through the soil. This way, the plant takes the water it needs and I replenish the reservoir every week or so. I get a bumper crop of tomatoes every summer without fail!

The point of the story is that the plant is the chief expert on how much water it needs, and given the right tool (in this case, the self-watering planter), it will take exactly the right amount throughout its growing cycle. Similarly, taking vitamin supplements is a poor second choice compared to having a healthy gut symbiote, because a healthy gut ecosystem knows exactly how much of any nutrient our body needs, and works with our body's absorption system to produce and manage the right amounts. Supplements disrupt this process and should strongly be discouraged.

I am not saying vitamin supplements are harmful. For instance, as we grow older, our body's absorption rate of vitamins naturally decreases and we might need supplements. But a healthy person should not need to take any supplements until they are in their fifties or sixties. Moreover, a lack of absorption of vitamins is itself a sign of disease. It is important to understand why this is happening, to arrive at the root cause of the disease and then find the best way to cure it.

Water and the Symbiote

Drinking water is the biggest source of illness that travellers face. Of course, the bottled water industry loves this fact and has misused it to convince millions of consumers that tap water is bad for them. But what is the truth, and why is our gut symbiote so weak when it comes to waterborne illnesses?

It is a fact of nature that human evolution did not take into account the jet age. Someone clearly forgot to send a memo to the gut symbiote explaining that people are going to be getting into planes and travelling to the other side of the world in a matter of hours, so please could you adapt to a wide variety of microbes? The composition of microbes in water differs from place to place, because raw tap water is a very local produce. Speaking of produce, in China, crops are sprayed with untreated sewage, and no one worries about public health issues; the gut symbiote of the Chinese have largely adapted to the view that once in a while some E. coli is going to drop in for a visit, it's nothing to worry about. Raw, untreated tap water is loaded with bacteria, amoeba, viruses, fungi, you name it. Most of these are incompatible with the human stomach habitat and get killed by stomach acid. But there are a few culprits that are hardier and can survive a dose of strong acid.

There is a small protozoan called Entamoeba histolytica, commonly known as amoeba, which, when ingested in sufficient quantities, will cause your stomach symbiote and your immune system to go crazy. This is usually the culprit when travellers come down with 'Delhi Belly' or 'Montezuma's Revenge'. In countries like India, over 90 per cent of the population have amoeba in their stomachs, and it has adapted to living there without causing a fuss. But in people who are exposed to it for the first time, it can feel like the human body is not just a bag of water (which it is), but a very leaky one!

The Science behind the Latest Fad Diet

Every year it seems like a new diet becomes the latest fashion. Some new guru rises to the surface with a best-selling book, endorsed by a celebrity or two, and suddenly everyone is trying it out. What is the mystery behind these diets, and why do they seem to work?

The first thing to note about diets and weight loss is this: every diet that involves a permanent reduction in the number of calories that we eat will result in weight loss. This is basic math. If you eat less, all other things being equal, fewer calories are converted to adipose fat in the body by the gut symbiote bacteria. We will discuss this in detail when we talk about the various types of bacteria in the gut.

On the other hand, if you eat the same amount of food but exercise more, you will also lose weight because you are burning more energy and you use up the excess carbs. Some people are able to regulate their diet and exercise patterns so that their body weight stays constant for their entire adult lives. But many of us are not able to do this, because we do not know how many calories we consume and how many we burn. It is just too complicated.

Enter the fad diet, which appears to take a lot of the guesswork out of dieting.

One of the most popular fad diets these days is the low-carb diet. People who go on it will eat anything but carbohydrates. This diet actually works because, in essence, the dieter is starving his gut firmicute bacteria of the carbs that they require to turn into adipose tissue. When this happens, the quantity of firmicutes in the gut is reduced. With fewer firmicutes, there is less fat storage and most of the calories in the non-carb food that is eaten simply passes unabsorbed through the body. The weight loss happens because the body starts using up its available stores of fat, with little replenishment.

It is worth noting that you only need a low-carb diet if the total food you consume every day is larger than your body's requirements. For people who eat what they need, and no more, a normal balanced diet works just fine. In fact, in many parts of Asia, people eat a largely carb-based diet with no noticeable obesity issues.

Bathroom Habits and Hygiene

We live in a world where social habits are dictated not by a proper understanding of hygiene but by our 'aversive emotions'. Let us look at the social faux pas of not washing your hands after going to the bathroom. Studies show that over one-third of all men are guilty of not washing after urinating.

But is this really bad from a hygiene standpoint? Actually, no, because urine is sterile. In fact, urine is so pure that before the age of antibiotics, surgeons would wash their implements in fresh urine! I am not suggesting that people stop washing their hands after urinating, I am merely pointing out that there is no hygiene reason for doing so, it is purely ornamental kowtow to an aversive emotion.

In Western societies, many people, women in particular, are prone to some degree of obsessive compulsive disorder. This manifests as an obsession with hygiene. The whole thing starts with a trigger of our aversive emotion, helped along by a good dose of television advertisements from disinfectant manufacturers showing green monster-like bugs invading your kitchen counters. This emotion is absent in infants and starts to manifest around the age of four. Until that age, children have no concept of being revolted by anything. Once the emotion starts, however, it is a lifelong affliction. There is a deep evolutionary basis for aversion or disgust, since it is essentially a mechanism to keep us away from human excrement and rotting flesh, both of which can harbour pathogenic agents.

However, as with any emotion, too much disgust is not a good thing, and people often get carried away by what puts them off. Let's separate fact from myth and see where it takes us.

I mentioned that urine is sterile and is nothing to worry about; defecating is another matter altogether. It is a very good idea to wash hands with soap after defecating, in order to wash out a type of bacteria called coliform bacteria which is present in faeces. Escherichia coli is the best known member of this type of bacteria, and it is not only the cause of the vast majority of bacterial stomach ailments, but it is also highly antibiotic-resistant. But a word on E. coli: it is everywhere that mammals live. On walls, on the floor, on furniture, in the air, it is the most ubiquitous species of bacteria found wherever humans live. So you can never get rid of it altogether. In minute quantities it is harmless, but in the concentration that it is found in human faeces, it can cause stomach illnesses, and in some very rare cases it can be deadly. In fact, one of the postulates of the hygiene hypothesis holds that a little E. coli around the house is a good thing because the immune system learns to deal with it. In homes that use excess hygiene to reduce E. coli, the paradox is that when the inhabitants get exposed to it outside the home they are likely to fall very sick. This is why children who grow up on farms are so healthy; their immune systems are robust, and their bodies are colonized by a robust symbiote to boot.

In fact, E. coli is one of the most studied bacteria in science. Its genome has been completely sequenced and we are close to unlocking its secrets. The pharmaceutical industry will no doubt try and find creative ways of fighting it.

But the fight against E. coli is doomed from the start because of its sheer ubiquity and its close evolution alongside the human species. What is needed instead is public policy designed to promote a benign strain of E. coli, one that does not cause any damage to humans, and then spread it widely. Let us learn to live with E. coli and make friends with it.

What about bathing? There is no doubt that a bath is refreshing, and smelling clean has social benefits that are compelling, but what does bathing do to the skin symbiote?

In general, we associate bathing with good hygiene. But this is because people who have poor sanitary habits when it comes to faeces also tend not to bathe. We therefore equate bathing with good sanitary habits, since we have no real way of knowing if someone washed their hands properly after defecating and cleaning themselves.

In reality, bathing itself is fairly benign as far as the symbiote is concerned. Certainly, billions of skin symbiote bacterial cells are washed down the drain, but they are replaced in a matter of minutes. Your skin will not stay under-colonized for long. Bathing is not particularly beneficial, but it is not harmful either. On the whole, it is a good idea to bathe regularly, given the societal and social benefits of bathing and smelling clean.

The Invisible Protector on Your Skin

There is a whole new school of thought regarding the role of a certain type of skin symbiote bacteria. When we sweat, we release some nitrous chemicals onto the skin. There is a whole ecosystem of bacteria that has adapted to living on these chemicals, and converting them into nitrogen amides. We know that amides are a powerful natural disinfectant. It is only logical to put two and two together and conjecture that sweat is good for you.

Aristotle said 'nature abhors a vacuum'. What he meant is that absence of any kind is not tolerated in nature, and any vacuum is quickly filled. This is particularly true in the microbial world, where a disinfected surface is re-colonized in seconds. This is why the notion that we can create and maintain a sterile surface is laughable, to say the least. The process of sterilization is essentially bringing a mechanical or chemical solution to bear upon an evolutionary problem. It's like asking evolution to come up with a way of getting around the problem. Either the microbes wait until the disinfectant evaporates (like alcohol-based ones do), or they evolve to survive the disinfectant. It is just a matter of time, and sooner or later all bacteria evolve around these fixes, and science has to go back to the drawing board. But the very approach of creating a biological vacuum is flawed. A better method would be to create a benign surface – a surface full of benign microbes that crowd out the pathogenic ones.

I foresee a day when hospitals no longer sterilize equipment by using disinfectant. Rather, they will spray a thin film of either good bacteria or neutral bacteria, so that every surface is covered by them. This will stop pathogenic bacteria from colonizing disinfected surfaces.

3

NITROGEN AND YOUR HEALTH

❧❦

Former US President George H.W. Bush hated broccoli. One of his famous quotes goes like this: 'I do not like broccoli and I haven't liked it since I was a little kid and my mother made me eat it. And I'm President of the United States and I'm not going to eat any more broccoli.'

This, of course, caused a predictable avalanche of broccoli to fall on Washington as the American farm lobby sent truckloads of the stuff to the White House. The episode was mainly hilarious, but it has a bittersweet ending. As it turned out, Mr Bush, whose favourite food was pork rinds (he loves the skin) and who was not a big vegetable eater, ended up with Graves' disease, which is a form of hyperthyroidism.

Graves' disease is an autoimmune disorder. President Bush's story is an interesting anecdote, but most people who contract Graves, are women between the ages of twenty and forty (in other words, of childbearing age), and the disease is up to eight times more prevalent among women than men. It does tend to run in families, so it has a genetic component. This is true for men in particular—where both parents have Graves', there is a good chance that their male children will get it (both of the elder Bush's parents had Graves').

You get hyperthyroidism when the thyroid gland produces too much of the thyroxine hormone. Genetic disposition aside, thyroxine production levels have a high inverse correlation to nitrates in a diet, meaning that eating food containing nitrates keeps the thyroid from over-secreting the hormone. And the raw vegetable that contains one of the highest levels of dietary nitrates? Broccoli![1]

We also know that Graves' disease, which is the cause of 70 per cent cases of hyperthyroidism, is linked to iron imbalance, because a third of women and 40 per cent men who show symptoms of Graves' are also anaemic, with low haemoglobin in their blood.[2] Treating Graves' disease with anti-thyroid compounds usually causes the anaemia to disappear.

What is the role of the gut symbiote in hyperthyroidism? There are a group of chemicals called nitrates, which we saw earlier in the discussion on hyperthyroidism, which are present in raw vegetables like spinach and broccoli and also in cabbage, cauliflower, kale and others. In the human body, these nitrates are converted into nitrite, and then into nitric oxide (NO) by several types of gut bacteria.[3] Nitric oxide has all kinds of beneficial effects on the body, and NO pathways in the body are responsible for everything from male erections to mood enhancement to muscle stamina.

Now here is an interesting observation: drinking fizzy drinks over many years is a known risk factor for hyperthyroidism.[4] Studies have long focused on the effects of artificial sweetener, caffeine or even the carbonation in drinks, but they have ignored one simple fact: people who drink fizzy drinks are drinking them instead of something else, and that something else is plain water. Humans evolved over millennia to drink water and to take essential minerals from it, yet about 70 per cent of the population in the developed world now sustains itself primarily with fizzy drinks. Where is the evolutionary basis for carbonated caffeinated sugar water?

Regular water contains about 20 per cent of the dietary intake of nitrates, although this number can be higher in rural areas where people drink well water next to fields that use nitrate fertilizers.

It is also generally true that people who drink a lot of carbonated drinks are the type of people who eat fried foods and less green leafy vegetables. Taken together, and over a period of time, a nitrate deficiency builds up, which causes the thyroid gland to go crazy.

Ironically, most health authorities in the US focus on excess nitrates in the drinking water, not a lack of nitrates in people who drink carbonated drinks. This is because of another unfortunate link. In infants under six months of age, drinking excess nitrates can cause a very serious illness called blue baby syndrome (the technical term is a tongue twister, methaemoglobinemia).[5] But why on earth are infants under six months drinking any kind of water in the first place, instead of drinking breast milk, which contains almost no nitrates? The answer is the infant formula industry, which has convinced generations of women that formula is just as good as breast milk. Well, this is debatable to say the least, but one thing is for sure: when you mix formula with water which has lots of nitrates, the result is blue baby syndrome. You see, human babies did not evolve to handle nitrates, because for thousands of years, they grew up drinking breast milk, until the infant formula industry came along. To make matters worse, it is not easy to rid drinking water of nitrates. If you boil the water, it actually causes nitrates to become concentrated!

Nitrates in water are pretty much harmless to adults and, in fact, are a necessary part of the adult diet. So health authorities all over the world should focus not on reducing dietary nitrates but on promoting breastfeeding of infants under six months. Thankfully, in India there is not much of a debate about this, but if you look at countries like the US, there is a significant percentage of mothers who only bottlefeed their infants.

Coming back to President Bush, the solution was as bad as his disease. A lifetime of not eating veggies had caught up with him, but he did not see the point of adjusting his diet and seeing if the effects of Graves' could be reversed. Instead, he pressed the nuclear button! As part of the standard, medically accepted 'cure' for Graves', he was taken to hospital where he drank a dose of radioactive iodine, which concentrated in his thyroid and literally fried it from the inside. After that, the 'ex-thyroid' stopped producing thyroxine in the ex-president's body. Like many others who followed this 'cure', he is now on a daily dose of artificial thyroxine for life.

It is terrifying to think that the cure for a hyperactive thyroid is a dose of radiation to kill the thyroid, followed by pills taken daily for life, but I am not making this up. People choose this type of cure every day instead of drinking broccoli juice for a couple of months, let alone treating this as a wake-up call and changing their lifestyle.

Let us now look at the other form of thyroid disorder, this one called hypothyroidism, which is the opposite of Graves' disease. Hypothyroidism is when the thyroid produces too little thyroxine. This ailment is primarily thought to be an autoimmune disorder caused by genetic factors, but there is another culprit that could trigger it. Often, hypothyroidism occurs right after you finish a course of antibiotics, so it is worth investigating to see if there is a symbiote balance issue in hypothyroidism. Well, it turns out there may well be, and the mechanism works like this.

What happens when you inadvertently blast the NO-producing bacteria living in the gut by using a Broad spectrum antibiotic? Hopefully they come back after you are done with the course. But sometimes they don't. This is when you run into big trouble. First, your NO balance in the body is upset; this can cause reduced sex drive, mood swings, depression and a host of other NO pathway-related problems, including inhibiting the effect of thyroxine in the blood. And then it gets worse. What happens to all the nitrates you get from the veggies you eat, which were previously being converted by the symbiote into nitrites and then NO? The human body adjusts to excess nitrates by increasing its tolerance. This tolerance, unfortunately, has consequences. The excess nitrates stick around in the body for a little while, long enough to further inhibit the production of thyroxine in the thyroid, because nitrates are a known thyroxine inhibitor.[6] In fact, the hormone thyroxine is itself an amino compound, meaning it contains nitrogen.

The result of low NO combined with excess nitrate is hypothyroidism. At the moment, this is an area that needs a more systematic exploration, but the role of certain types of gut symbiote bacteria in NO production is very real, and the effects of NO in the human body in balanced quantities are also known to be beneficial.

An interesting footnote relates to research that focuses on how hypothyroidism inhibits NO formation.[7] But what if the converse is true and the lack of or impairment in NO formation is a potential cause of hypothyroidism?

What is the solution to hypothyroidism? Paradoxically, in the short term you have to cut down on fresh vegetables, particularly members of the brassica family like broccoli, cabbage and cauliflower, since your body may be accumulating too many nitrates (these vegetables have large amounts of a form of nitrate called thiocyanate). Cooked vegetables have fewer nitrates so that is no problem. For some people, eating fewer vegetables might help if there is enough thyroxine being made but it is simply being inhibited by the nitrates. But the real solution is to get back the gut bacteria that break down the nitrates. Since some probiotics (which contain bifidobacteria) can do this, it is worth going to the supermarket and buying a couple of samples of all the probiotics that are available, and trying them one at a time over a week or so to see if there is any difference to your health. Until medicine figures out how to inoculate the gut with targeted bacterial strains that are good for you, the process of attempting to cure hypothyroidism is one of trial and error in the probiotic aisle of the supermarket.

What Do Beetroot Juice, Meditation and Dynamite Have in Common?

One of the most famous explosives, used in everything from commercial demolitions to war, is nitroglycerin (Glyceryl trinitrate). When you soak sawdust in nitroglycerin, you get a powerful explosive with a name most readers are familiar with—dynamite.

Besides being a powerful explosive, nitroglycerin has a key role to play in human health; it happens to be one of the oldest heart medications in use. In the human body, it works by converting into NO, which is an essential cellular messenger for a host of functions in the human body, including regulating blood pressure.

In fact, NO is so important to health that there is an entire branch of medical research devoted to understanding the NO balance in the human body. The reason I say 'balance' is because NO is both beneficial as well as harmful. While it is an essential cellular messenger, it is also a dangerous free radical when present in the body for any length of time. The body therefore regulates NO by converting it into nitrites and nitrates which are more inert, as we saw in the previous section on thyroid disorders. When NO is required, it produced by breaking down nitrites and nitrates in a mechanism that is still not well understood by science.

Nitric oxide imbalance is either the cause or the result of virtually every single chronic human health problem. Fixing this imbalance is therefore a key element in treating chronic illnesses. Since science is still evolving an understanding of this hugely complex issue, and until there are more studies and data points that can illuminate the NO balance, there are three important things you need to know about the NO/nitrite/nitrate balance:

1. Eating green leafy vegetables in moderate quantities is beneficial because they contain nitrates, which help

maintain the NO balance. For people with high blood pressure/hypertension, a glass of beetroot juice (also full of nitrates) has been shown to lower blood pressure.[8]

2. Meditation has been proven to increase NO levels, thereby lowering blood pressure.[9] The mechanism for this is not understood, but it is likely to do with the brain's ability to control the adrenal and thyroid glands, which are both very important in the NO balance.

3. The bacterial composition of your saliva, your stomach and your gut is extremely important in maintaining the NO balance, because bacteria convert nitrates into nitrites, which are then converted into NO by the body. This is yet another argument against the indiscriminate use of Broad spectrum antibiotics.

Economy Class Syndrome or the 'Just Say NO' Problem

Steven just got laid off from work, when his office in London, an investment firm, shut down during the credit crunch. After being unemployed for six months, Steven was quite stressed out. He needed a break from London, and decided to go trekking for a month in Ladakh. Ladakh is at an average elevation of 10,000 feet above sea level, a height where it is quite difficult to spend any length of time without the body acclimatizing to it. During the trek, Steven was caught in a landslide and cut off from the nearest village for several days. It was a particularly stressful time, and Steven was beginning to wonder if perhaps he should have spent the summer in sunny London after all, playing cricket and drinking beer. Steven finally arrived in Bombay after the trek, and woke up one morning with a painful, swollen leg. The doctors diagnosed Deep Vein Thrombosis (DVT). He had to spend the next four months in India, as he was not allowed to fly.

The causes of DVT are not well understood, but there are several factors that point to an NO connection. High blood pressure increases DVT risk, and NO is probably the most important blood pressure regulator. At high altitudes, blood pressure naturally increases in the lungs, because of lower levels of oxygen in the air. But the most intriguing connection with NO is this: people who live at high altitudes, particularly Tibetans, have levels of NO in their lungs that are seven times that of people living at sea level.[10]

In Steven's case, it is very likely that stress played a major role, by increasing his blood pressure and lowering his NO, when he needed higher NO due to the increased altitude. It is too early to conclude whether beetroot juice or nitroglycerin tablets should be taken as a preventive measure for DVT, particularly by trekkers, but if I were going to Ladakh, I would certainly drink some beetroot juice beforehand.

A Bit of Traditional Medicine

Traditional Chinese medicine (TCM) has been practised

for thousands of years. Every traditional form of medicine that has evolved in human history seems to have a particular focus, and TCM's focus seems to be cardiovascular or heart treatments. Many Western doctors are quite dismissive of what they derogatorily term 'alternative medicine', and this is largely because you don't often see a direct pharmacological agent when you analyze TCM in Western laboratories. But what if TCM contains a precursor rather than the actual agent? It would not be readily picked up, particularly when the lab does not know what it is looking for. It turns out that TCM, particularly that used for cardiovascular treatments, does have these precursors. TCMs are full of nitrates and nitrites, which are converted into NO in the body.[11] You would expect that for any heart problems caused by a shortage of NO, traditional Chinese medicine would be an interesting approach.

4

IRON AND YOUR HEALTH

❧

Oxidative stress is a constant theme in the human body. Eating and breathing contribute to it, and we spend a lot of time doing both. Sleeping reduces it, and gives the body's repair mechanism a chance to rest for a while.

However, there is one other method by which we seem to produce free radicals, this time on a continuous basis and with no respite for the body's repair mechanism. This is caused by the presence of excess iron in cells. Iron in the human body is carefully regulated. But, according to a wide body of evidence, excess iron causes a steady amount of oxidative stress.[1] The problem with this kind of stress is that it is constant, and it increases rapidly as the amount of iron in cells increases. Over time, the damage due to this is enormous.

The role and function of iron in our body is probably the single most serious issue regarding human health. Iron is one of the most dangerous chemicals in the human body, when there is either too much or too little of it. Medical science has focused on the dangers of anaemia or low iron, but what about superfluous iron?

Excessive iron has been implicated in a stunning array of diseases from skin infections to Parkinson's, from heart disease to osteoporosis, from skin cancer to lung infections. When we talk about extending human lifespan and enjoying a healthy life free of chronic illness right up until the end, we must remember that the right iron balance is essential, particularly during middle age and beyond.

There are three measures of iron in the human body: haemoglobin, ferritin and transferrin. The three indicate the different forms in which iron is stored in the body.

The medical community defines normal levels of haemoglobin to be somewhere between 11.5 and 16 gm/dL, but some guidelines state that it is between 12 and 18 for females and between 13 and 18 for males. The problem with these ranges is that what is normal can vary from individual to individual, given that these are averages. For most people these ranges will make sense – a woman with a level of eight is most likely anaemic, and a man with a level of 24 probably has a condition called hemochromatosis, in which dangerous levels of iron build up in the blood. But between these extreme iron levels, having even a minor imbalance from your body's ideal level can cause minor symptoms that can turn into long-term negative consequences for your health. But how do you figure out what is the normal level of iron for you? The first thing is to do a blood test during your regular checkup and see that the level is within the ranges mentioned above. If you are in good health, that iron level is most likely the correct level for you. But if you have symptoms of any of the diseases in the table on the next page, there is every chance that your iron levels are out of balance. It is also likely that the diseases themselves cause iron levels to be thrown off-balance, but whether the iron balance is a result of cause or effect is less important than the imperative to balance the iron levels.

The essentials for good health start with a healthy focus on the symbiote and how to keep it in balance. Recall that the symbiote is merely an evolutionary machine, meaning that it has no particular altruistic purpose other than its own survival. We can engage with this machine either in a positive way by assessing its needs and keeping it in a healthy balance, or in a negative way by fighting it at every turn and treating it like a pathogenic breeding ground. I strongly believe that the former approach is preferable, because it is easier to implement. Fighting an evolutionary machine is an impossible task, because whatever you do, the machine learns, evolves, improves and comes back stronger in the next round.

Striking a balance with an evolutionary machine is much easier; the machine is by and large self-regulating, and you can simply let the machine run on its own as long as it causes no harm.

You will find below two tables that I have constructed, listing the kind of diseases caused by iron imbalance. These show that virtually every part of the body is affected by iron imbalance.

TABLE 1. ILLNESSES CAUSED BY EXCESS IRON		
Area affected	**Disease**	**Incidence**
Bones	Osteoporosis	Post-menopausal females
Brain	Parkinson's disease	Males/post-menopausal females
Colon	Colon cancer	Males/post-menopausal females
Heart	Heart disease, arrhythmia, heart muscle disease	Males/post-menopausal females
Joints	Gout, infection-related arthritis	Males/post-menopausal females
Liver	Viral hepatitis, cirrhosis, cancers	Males/post-menopausal females
Lungs	Lung cancer	Males/post-menopausal females
Pancreas	Cancer	Males/post-menopausal females

Pituitary glands	Testes and growth dysfunction	Males
Skin	Leprosy, skin cancer, staph infections	Males/post-menopausal females
Soft tissue	Cancer	Males/post-menopausal females
White blood cells	Intracellular infections	Males/post-menopausal females

TABLE 2. DISEASES CAUSED BY LACK OF IRON		
Area affected	**Disease**	**Incidence**
Blood circulation	Cold hands and feet, tingling	Mainly females
Brain	Headache	Mainly females
Heart	Irregular heartbeat	Mainly females
Lungs	Shortness of breath	Mainly females
Immune system	Allergies	Mainly females
Skin	Pale skin and brittle nails	Mainly females
Body	Extreme fatigue	Mainly females
Diet	Cravings for non-edible foods	Mainly females
Reproductive	Menstruation stops	Females

It is important to understand that iron imbalance causes a vast majority of illnesses. Once we identify this, treatment can focus on the root cause of the iron imbalance.

You will notice from the table on pages 78–9 a distinct pattern in terms of who is affected by iron imbalances and what form the imbalance takes. Men are more prone to excess iron in their blood, usually as a result of excess red meat consumption or some other cause of excess iron intake. Women are more prone to anaemia because they lose iron during menstrual bleeding. This can be exacerbated if there is some kind of asymptomatic bleeding in the stomach or an internal organ. Very few men are diagnosed with anaemia, compared to women.

When women undergo menopause, their iron levels go up and can easily tip into excess. The risk of heart problems among men is twice as high between the ages of forty-five and seventy-four than among women. Clearly, women have a two-decade window after menopause while their iron levels catch up. After the age of seventy-five, heart problems occur more or less evenly.

But if you look at autoimmune diseases like arthritis, the picture is the opposite: women between the ages of forty-five and seventy-four have a much higher incidence of arthritis than men.

Iron is an essential mineral that plays a dual role in the body: metabolism and oxygen transfer. Around 65 per cent of the iron in your body is found in haemoglobin, which

TABLE 3. LONGSTANDING ILLNESS BY SEX, AGE AND CONDITION, 2007, GREAT BRITAIN

		All ages %	16-44 %	45-64 %	65-74 %	75+ %
Heart and circulatory system	Men	10.9	1.0	14.7	32.0	33.8
	Women	9.7	1.8	11.0	23.9	27.7
	Both	10.3	1.4	12.8	27.7	30.1
Heart attack	Men	1.8	0.0	2.2	6.5	5.7
	Women	1.1	0.1	0.8	2.6	5.1
Other heart complaints	Men	3.6	0.3	4.6	10.2	12.1
	Women	2.8	0.6	2.8	6.5	9.6
Stroke	Men	0.8	0.0	0.8	2.8	3.8
	Women	0.5	0.1	0.5	1.2	1.9
Blood vessel/embolic disorders	Men	0.9	0.2	0.9	2.3	3.9
	Women	0.7	0.4	0.8	1.0	1.1
Musculoskeletal system	Men	12.2	5.5	16.2	23.4	25.8
	Women	16.3	6.0	20.1	30.8	38.4
	Both	14.3	5.7	18.2	27.3	33.3
Arthritis and rheumatism	Men	5.3	1.2	6.8	13.7	15.2
	Women	8.7	1.5	11.3	19.6	23.3
Respiratory system	Men	5.7	4.6	4.8	9.4	11.5
	Women	6.1	5.0	6.7	7.9	7.4
	Both	5.9	4.8	5.8	8.6	9.0

		All ages %	16-44 %	45-64 %	65-74 %	75+ %
Asthma	Men	3.7	3.8	3.0	4.2	5.1
	Women	4.6	4.4	5.0	4.9	3.8
Endocrine and metabolic	Men	4.9	1.4	7.0	11.7	10.8
	Women	5.8	1.8	8.4	10.5	11.8
	Both	5.4	1.6	7.7	11.0	11.4
Digestive system	Men	2.5	1.4	3.2	4.4	3.8
	Women	3.6	2.1	4.9	5.6	4.8
	Both	3.1	1.7	4.1	5.0	4.4
Nervous system	Men	2.6	1.6	3.8	3.5	3.2
	Women	3.4	2.7	4.0	4.7	3.9
	Both	3.0	2.1	3.9	4.1	3.6
Any longstanding illness	Men	31.0	20.0	43.0	60.0	66.0
	Women	32.0	22.0	41.0	56.0	65.0
	Both	31.0	21.0	42.0	58.0	65.0
Weighted base (000s)	Men	22,846	11,594	7,245	2,309	1,698
	Women	24,165	11,610	7,484	2,558	2,512
Unweighted base	Men	8,180	3,540	2,820	1,070	740
	Women	8,950	3,920	2,970	1,130	930

Notes: Data are weighted for non-response.
Source: Office for National Statistics (2009) Results from the 2007 General Household Survey. www.ons.gov.uk/ghs

is a protein in red blood cells that literally carries oxygen to your body's tissues. Smaller amounts of iron are found in myoglobin, protein that carries oxygen to the muscles. About 15 per cent of your body's iron is stored as a reserve to maintain iron balance and is used when dietary intake is not enough. The remainder of the iron is stored in your body's tissues as part of other proteins that are essential to various body functions.

At a very basic level, iron levels are balanced in healthy individuals because the body is a very efficient machine. Generally speaking, the body tends to be fairly conservative in absorbing iron. We lose about one milligram a day through sweat or dead skin cells, but at all times we have 3.5 grams of iron within our body. However, since the main way of losing a significant amount of the accumulated iron in the body is through bleeding, iron absorption tends to be a one-way street. In other words, with the exception of women who menstruate regularly, most people slowly accumulate iron in their body over time. The body adjusts to this; this is why most of the iron we eat simply passes through the body, unless the levels are low and need replenishing.

The right level of iron in the body depends on the level of physical activity we engage in. Iron is absolutely essential for metabolism and oxygen transfer to tissues and muscles. This is why the chief symptom of anaemia is fatigue. If you are short of iron, you cannot perform physical activities like sports or simple daily chores. In fact, the body becomes even more efficient at using its iron stores as iron levels fall. We know, for example, that anaemic women stop menstruating, which is the body's way of maintaining iron levels by literally stopping the bleeding!

The medical world is well-versed in the symptoms of anaemia, and iron tablets are usually prescribed to treat it. But iron tablets don't really work for anaemic people. If it were a simple matter of taking a few pills to cure anaemia, hardly anyone in the developed world would have chronic anaemia! The reality is that up to a third of the world's population has some form of anaemia, largely as a result of malnutrition and under-nutrition. Anaemia is a serious illness, but the body can and does adapt by becoming more efficient at managing its stores of iron. At the same time, the iron you ingest has to be in a form that is bio-available in order for the body to absorb it from food.

The problem, though, is in the definition of iron deficiency. In the United States, studies show that only one in ten women is iron deficient. This may be true if you define iron deficiency as showing symptoms of anaemia. But there is a case to be made that any autoimmune disorder should be seen as a symptom of iron deficiency; at the very least, when there is an immune disorder one should check iron levels and eliminate low iron as a cause of the disorder before looking for other causes.

Now here is a simple solution for anaemia and borderline

anaemia: go to the store and buy yourself a heavy cast iron skillet. Cook yourself a lovely pasta with tinned tomatoes (or even fresh ones) on that skillet, about twice a week. It's as simple as that. Tomatoes are mildly acidic, tinned tomatoes even more so. When you cook tomatoes in an iron skillet, a little bit of the iron rubs off onto the pasta, in a form that is easily absorbed by the body.

But there are many people, mainly men but also post-menopausal women, who have the opposite problem – they have borderline iron overload or excess iron in their bodies.

Although the medical community has largely ignored the problem of iron overload, one can see an epidemic of excess iron-related diseases in the Western world such as the ones described in Table 3.

The reason why iron overload is a major issue is simple. In the human body, there is no good way to naturally eliminate excess iron. Why is this? Why has this beautiful evolutionary machine not been able to figure out how to get rid of excess iron, like it does all other manner of waste product?

The answer is actually quite simple. As far as nature is concerned, we are not meant to live beyond the age of thirty-five! Nature and evolution select characteristics that are passed on to the next generation,which help the next generation cope with their natural environment. Since humans have historically had their offspring in their mid-teens, and then brought up their offspring until *their* teens by the age of thirty-five or so, nature doesn't really care how much longer we survive beyond that age! In a very sense, extending human lifespans is unnatural, but of course it is desirable and it is the ultimate yardstick of progress. We now live in an era where life *begins* not just at thirty-five, but even at seventy! To put it mildly, the reason nature did not build an iron elimination mechanism in the human machine is because iron overloading happens after the age of thirty, and nature doesn't really care how much longer we live beyond that age.

Having crossed the age of thirty-five some years ago, I care deeply about contravening nature and extending human lifespans to the magic figure of 100, while maintaining good health and a high quality of life.

Consider the field of geriatric research, which has seen a frenzied growth in modern medicine, not least because the Western world is aging rapidly. It doesn't hurt that most of the wealth in the West is in the hands of older folks, so there is a tremendous financial incentive for the medical community to come up with solutions that extend lifespans and increase the quality of life.

However, the whole medical field has been hijacked by the 'chronic care' mechanism which I talked about in the introduction. Doctors are paid per visit, and they also make money on tests. This ultimately leads to a situation where the whole approach to health becomes the management of a chronic disease like diabetes or a progressive disease like Alzheimer's, rather than trying to figure out the root cause of why we get sick and try to cure it at the source.

We know, for example, that the symptoms of old age are linked to the accumulation of waste products in cells over time. Obviously, if someone could figure out how to rid the cells of these waste products, you could stop and even reverse the effects of aging. Science is working on all these things and there are exciting discoveries and potential treatments on the way. But in the meantime, let us look at the other substance that accumulates in the body over time, which we can get rid of quite easily and at no cost at all. I am talking, of course, of iron.

We saw the incredible range of illnesses in Table 1, affecting virtually every part of the body. These are all tied to excess iron build-up. Iron build-up is usually gradual, as the efficient human body minimizes the absorption rate of dietary iron if it feels that the iron stores in the body are adequate. But while the absorption rate can be minimized, it cannot be cut to zero, because *some* iron from our diet will get through the digestion process and into our blood stream. At any event, you don't want to cut iron absorption to zero, because we do lose a little bit of it each day through sweat and from bacterial action within our body.

There are two forms of dietary iron: heme and non-heme. Heme is found in red meat, and to a lesser extent in fish and poultry. Non-heme iron is found in plants like spinach, and a little bit in meat. Non-heme iron is easy for the body to deal with from an excess standpoint, because it is harder to absorb. If the iron balance in the body is adequate, non-heme iron passes right through. But heme iron is different; because it is so easily absorbed, a little gets into the body every time we eat red meat, even if the levels of iron in the body are adequate. This causes no immediate symptoms, but the effects of a red meat diet are cumulative. The iron keeps building up, ever so slowly, and after a few decades, this certainly matters! Most excess iron illnesses affect people from middle to old age. This should not come as a surprise, given what we know about the cumulative effects of dietary iron.

The body defines iron balance essentially as a condition in which the level of iron is adequate for performing the functions that the body is normally involved in. In other words, star athletes need more iron than couch potatoes do. Therefore, a higher level of iron in star athletes is not a problem, but in people with sedentary lifestyles, the same levels can cause problems. The medical community uses a fixed range of iron levels in what it considers to be 'normal', and as long as the levels are close to that range, they don't see a problem. Consider this sad example as an illustration.

A seventy-eight-year-old man, quite an athlete in his younger days and still a very active player of team sports, went in for a hip replacement. While in hospital, he acquired a staph infection, which required him to be treated with antibiotics and to stay in the hospital for three months. While he was recuperating from the staph infection, he developed a blood stream infection of gram-negative bacteria called acinetobacter. None of the antibiotics worked for this infection, and he died.

There are two major issues here. The first is that the Broad spectrum antibiotics used to treat his staph infection destroyed a good part of his skin and gut symbiote, leaving him vulnerable to the acinetobacter. Acinetobacter is immune to common antibiotics, but the gram-positive skin symbiote bacteria are not. It is entirely possible that treating the staph with antibiotics allowed the opportunistic acinetobacter to take hold in the blood stream, with fatal consequences. The second issue is significant: at no point was his level of iron checked. As a former athlete on a red meat diet, it is likely that he had excess iron in his blood, which caused not only the staph, but also the acinetobacter to take hold, which ultimately killed him.

The first thing that the hospital should have done was check his iron, but this is not part of the current medical thought process. Even if they had, they would have considered the 'normal' ranges and seen that perhaps he had an iron of 16 gm/dL, which is at the high end of the 11–16 normal range, but nothing to worry about.

How are these 'normal' ranges calculated? Are these differentiated by levels of fitness, activity and age? Of course not. The only concession made is that of sex, i.e., women have a wider range at the lower end because of menstruation.

But the reality is that this patient was highly active until he went in for his hip replacement surgery. Sixteen gm/dL may have been fine to support this level of physical activity. But he was then on a hospital bed for three months, and his iron levels did not change during that time. They may even have gone up if he ate the meat-laden hospital food. Is 16gm/dL an appropriate blood iron level for someone on a hospital bed for three months? Unlikely. This is probably what contributed to his death by letting the acinetobacter infect his blood stream.

Although there are many examples where healthy, active people go into a hospital for a procedure and end up dying of a hospital-acquired infection, it is shocking that very little research has been done on the normal level of iron in the human body. It should be obvious that hospital-acquired infections are iron related, since few women of menstruating age are affected.

We have already seen that most pathogenic bacteria are actually normal members of the symbiote that have 'gone rogue'. In the next section, we will examine why this happens.

Staphaureus belongs to a family of bacteria called gram-positive bacteria. This is the same family to which firmicutes like H. pylori belong. Gram-positive bacteria are very different from their biological cousins, gram-negative bacteria, so it is worth looking at the two categories separately.

S. aureus, like many other bacterial species, has co-evolved with humans, and has been part of our symbiote since the time we evolved. It lives on our skin and in our noses, and is benign for the most part. But in certain circumstances it can enter and infect the blood stream, heart, lungs or bones, and then becomes responsible for a range of infections. It is responsible for the vast majority of hospital-acquired infections, and it has acquired a resistance to all common antibiotics in use today.

Yoshi was a star athlete and captain of his school football team. In his second year in high school, he found a small boil on his right buttock. A week later, it had swollen into a red, blistering mountain that radiated pain with every step. Slowly, the red blister turned yellow as it filled with pus, and a week later it burst, draining all the pus and providing relief to a now bedridden Yoshi. Yoshi's relief turned to dismay when he found two small new boils on his buttock two days after the first one burst. Yoshi went to see the doctor at last, who prescribed a course of antibiotics. This did not help with the two new boils, which continued to grow and finally had to be lanced by the doctor two weeks later, but it stopped the boil count at three. Yoshi had no more boils for six months, and then he found a new boil on his left thigh. The doctor again put him on antibiotics, but this cycle continued for years with no relief, no matter what antibiotics were tried. Unable to play during episodes of boils, Yoshi decided to give up football.

It was six years before Yoshi finally went to see an

Ayurvedic therapist. The therapist listened patiently to Yoshi's story, and suggested a very strange remedy. He told Yoshi to go to the nearest blood donation centre and donate a pint of blood. He further told Yoshi to donate blood every six months. Yoshi was sceptical, but went ahead and followed the therapist's advice. Ten years later, Yoshi is yet to see a boil anywhere on his body.

This is perhaps the most significant idea in this book. It turns out that the concentration of iron in the blood stream is directly proportional to the number and potency of bacterial infections that you experience. When Yoshi donated a pint of blood, he automatically reduced the amount of iron in his blood to below the threshold where he was prone to bacterial infections such as boils.

Throughout history, and before the use of antibiotics became widespread in the early twentieth century, the standard cure for most ailments was a course of bloodletting. It is likely that humans discovered by chance that losing a certain amount of blood actually improved the condition of patients with different ailments, but the reason for this was not understood.

The same thought process went into another form of bloodletting called leech therapy. This was practised by ancient Egyptians nearly 4,000 years ago, and independently by the Greeks and the Chinese, as well as the ancient Indians. The ancient Indian physician Susrutha wrote extensively about leech therapy in 600 BCE. In recent history, this treatment was extremely popular in France and Portugal as late as the nineteenth century.

During leech therapy, a practitioner attaches a leech to an appropriate part of the body. The leech bite is not painful, and the leech itself extracts only about 5 millilitres of blood, which is an insignificant amount. However, the site of the leech bite continues to bleed until about 50 millilitres ooze out. This is because leech saliva contains a powerful anticoagulant called hirudin, which prevents the blood from clotting. In fact, hirudin is so powerful that it is known to cause bleeding in the gastrointestinal tract, so leech therapy is not recommended for people with peptic ulcers.

Of course, bloodletting does not work for every disease, but it does work wonders for one disease that has been the bane of human existence for millennia – staph infections.

Staph aureus is a grape-like cluster of golden-coloured bacteria. It is a tiny organism, only six microns wide. But for reasons that are not widely understood, it turns into a virulent pathogen in some people, even though it causes no problems in the vast majority. In medieval times, it caused boils or furuncles in some men, not unlike our friend Yoshi's case, and these boils could actually merge into a giant prurient pus-filled abscess known as a carbuncle, which is a life-threatening condition. It was this condition that bloodletting mostly cured. In places as far apart as Europe and India, medieval doctors would recommend bloodletting as a cure for carbuncles. With the advent of modern antibiotics, it was thought that staph aureus was finally defeated, along with other infectious bacterial illnesses caused by pathogens. We know better now, as the misuse of antibiotics has led to strains of staph that were first resistant to penicillin, then meticillin, and now vancomycin, which are three potent antibiotics in modern medicine's arsenal.

But the real question is this: why do we treat staph aureus as a pathogen when it lives harmlessly on the bodies of many, if not most, people? Why not think about the mechanism by which it becomes virulent, and try and deactivate that instead?

Since the emergence of antibiotics as a potent weapon, doctors have had a simple and effective tool at their disposal to treat staph infections. You just go to the doctor and get a course of antibiotics, and the infection goes away. But it is only in the past few years that medicine has begun to wake up to the dangers of antibiotics. It is not just the fact that staph has become resistant to most antibiotics, it is also that the antibiotics themselves have side effects. And most importantly, antibiotics treated staph symptoms but did not address the core issue of why staph becomes pathogenic sometimes.

Five years ago, scientists took the first step to understanding staph when they figured out how the mechanism of abscess formation works.[2] In essence, an abscess formation has a number of steps. First, staph takes hold in a particular spot just below the skin surface. They multiply for the next three hours until they reach a certain critical mass. After this they enter a quiet period of two to three days. During this time, the human body senses that there is a foreign intruder and tries to seal off the area, which is when the hard body of the abscess or boil begins to form and the inflammation begins. After two to three days, the staph bacteria start multiplying again, but this time there is an additional critical step called 'quorum sensing'. Quorum sensing is something many, if not most, bacterial species do. It is simply a process of detecting that a critical quantity of bacteria is present. When quorum sensing occurs, bacteria typically perform a specific task, such as producing a chemical. In this case, the staph start producing a toxin within the abscess, which causes the pain and symptoms. Scientists have discovered that a simple step of interfering with the quorum sensing can stop the abscess formation in its tracks, because the staph no longer produces the toxin. The abscess still forms, but it is a sterile one which is painless and does no harm. This is now leading the way to the development of all sorts of medicines that can stop bacteria from quorum sensing.[3]

If this approach leads to an increase in the number of disease fighting tools available to doctors, I am all for it. But it still does not address the issue of why symbiote staph bacteria form abscesses in the human host in the first place.

It just so happens that the answer to this question was figured out in ancient times by cultures as independent and diverse as the ancient Indians, medieval Europeans and even the ancient Incas of South America. The answer, of course, is excess iron. The ancients did not know it was excess iron, but they figured out that if some blood was removed from the patient, the infection disappeared. In the modern era, bloodletting has gone completely out of favour. This is unfortunate because a hugely cost-effective and important cure is being sidelined. The cynical view here is that the reasons for this are economic – the pharmaceutical industry makes no money from bloodletting.

Let us examine the evidence for the role of iron in bacterial infections, by looking at who is most prone to staph infections. When you think of healthy people coming down with staph infections, inevitably you find that most patients are male. Drug-resistant staph infection, in the United States in particular, seems to be widespread in the gay (male) community. There is, however, one type of staph infection known as mastitis which is common among breastfeeding women. Also, hospital-acquired staph infections affect not only men but older women too. What men, breastfeeding women and older women have in common is that they tend to have excess iron. Young women, on the other hand, tend not to because of menstruation, so they are not affected as much.

Given the use of bloodletting in history and the strong likelihood that iron is the culprit for staph infections, you would think that anyone who shows up at the doctor with a staph infection would immediately be checked for blood iron and asked to donate a pint of blood. But this almost never happens. Instead, they are put on a course of antibiotics, which may temporarily clear up the infection but does nothing to solve the underlying excess of iron. With the amount of red meat in Western diets, people consume plenty of iron, and sometimes this causes problems. The simple act of donating blood regularly cures this problem, as well as the problem of shortage of blood in blood banks.

Iron is the catalyst in many biological actions. In laboratory petri dish experiments, iron is used to promote bacterial growth. In fact, today there is a serious experiment being conducted to fight global warming by promoting blooms of algae in the open ocean, with the view that these algae will convert carbon dioxide into carbon biomass. The method being used to accomplish this algae bloom is to seed the test area of the ocean with iron.[4] So the role of iron in a variety of related fields is well known, but hardly anyone in the modern era has thought about its role in the human body and in infections. If you are male, you are well advised never to take iron supplements. If you are prone to skin infections, you should become a regular blood donor. You should minimize your intake of red meat, which not only produces harmful free radicals in the gut during the digestive process but also increases the iron in your blood, which is not a good thing if you are a man or a post-menopausal woman. These are simple steps that can control the spread of staph infections.

But I would go even further. S. aureus is a member of the human symbiote. It is not merely benign, but actually pays rent to the human host. Aureus and its close cousin pyogenes play a role in reducing inflammation on the outer skin by releasing a certain chemical.

So why not think of S. aureus as a signal? We have seen earlier how damaging excess iron can be in the body, leading to a range of diseases. A staph skin infection is not only a wake-up call to excess iron in the body, it is a mechanism that leaches excess iron out of the body. The infection usually takes the form of boils, and in the age before antibiotics were discovered, the infection would go when enough blood was lost through bursting boils or abscesses. Modern medicine now intervenes in staph infections by using antibiotics, but without treating the underlying iron excess, with potentially disastrous consequences. The staph symbiote is only doing its job, which is getting rid of excess iron by forming an abscess that then leaches the iron out of the body. We are best served when the prescription is to reduce iron levels in the blood at the first sign of a staph infection, given that this itself is a symptom of a larger issue!

Staph is an opportunistic bacterium. It is your friend only in that it is well adjusted to your body, but let us not forget that people die from staph infections all the time, so it is not to be taken lightly if you get an infection. By all means stop abscesses from forming and stop the infection using antibiotics, but the only way to reliably prevent the infection from recurring is to eliminate the root cause, excess iron.

Malaria and the Clues It Offers Iron Balance

Research has shown that in many tropical countries where malaria is common, men are far more likely to contract malaria than women. This is because the protozoan that causes malaria needs a certain level of iron in the blood in order to multiply in the human host. Men are more likely to have excess iron, and therefore more likely to contract malaria.

How did we discover this amazing fact? It turns out that the answer lies in a genetic condition called sickle-cell anaemia, which is common in Africa. Many people carry a single copy of the sickle-cell gene and lead normal lives. But when two carriers of the sickle-cell anaemia gene reproduce, some of their off-spring can end up with two copies of the gene, which then causes the debilitating illness called sickle-cell anaemia, which results in all sorts of nasty symptoms and ultimately a short lifespan. Scientists were initially baffled about how this gene survived evolution, given that it is a painful condition that immensely shortens the life expectancy of its sufferers. It was then discovered that the sickle-cell gene provides very good immunity from malaria. In other words, people who carry one copy of this gene have less iron in their blood, and are less likely to catch malaria.

If you look at the map of Africa where sickle-cell anaemia is common, you see that it exactly matches the map of Africa where malaria is common. Mystery solved![5] This disease offers a clue to how crucial iron levels in the blood are for malaria, and also for all sorts of so-called vector-borne diseases. It is also not surprising that men are much more susceptible to vector-borne diseases than women, given their higher iron levels.

We have seen how staph infections are uncommon among women who menstruate every month. but this does not mean there are no afflictions among women of child-bearing age. Although bacterial infections are far less common in women than men, women are more prone to anaemia due to a shortage of iron. Anemia is a full-fledged disease that has a weakening effect on the symbiote. This is because symbiote bacteria also need iron to stay healthy, and a lack of it means they are not healthy enough to do their job, which is to keep pathogens at bay. When this happens, the immune system kicks into overdrive in order to compensate, just like weak stomach muscles can lead to a bad back. This immune system overdrive in turn can cause a number of autoimmune diseases, from lupus to endometriosis, rheumatoid arthritis to asthma. It is not surprising that women of child-bearing age are more prone to autoimmune diseases, given that they are likely to have too little iron in their blood. Crucially, iron balance plays a big role in autoimmune diseases, as we shall see.

Death Wish 6: Raw Oysters

Michael Winner is known to many Londoners as the food critic of *The Sunday Times* and the director of the *Death Wish* movies. A gourmet and a bon vivant, Michael has lived a life of fine dining and high living that a lot of us can only dream of. But in January 2007, at the age of seventy-two, Michael nearly died from eating a raw oyster in Barbados.

Many of us love to eat raw oysters. Despite the scaremongering media, oysters are a safe and tasty treat when handled properly. However, like most things in life, there is a tiny but significant risk in eating them. According to the US Centers for Disease Control (CDC), 5,000 Americans die every year from foodborne diseases, and of these, around 250 are caused by eating raw oysters. Out of a US population of 300 million, 250 is not a lot, but it is nevertheless worth looking closely at the pathogenic bacteria that cause oyster-borne illness. This bacterium is called Vibrio vulnificus, and it is a cousin of Vibrio cholerae, the more common bacteria that causes cholera. V. vulnificus is the same bacteria that nearly killed Michael Winner.

Interestingly, V. vulnificus illnesses occur mostly in people over the age of fifty, and 85 per cent of the deaths occur in men.[6] But this is no surprise, because V. vulnificus invades the blood stream and causes septic shock. As a study showed nearly thirty years ago, there is a direct correlation between the levels of iron in the blood and the virulence and deadliness of a V. vulnificus infection.[7] The solution is to use drugs to leach iron out, or simply to remove enough blood to starve the pathogen of iron. For someone there were Michael Winner's lifestyle, with steaks and lamb chops and liver and kidney on offer at every turn, and it would be interesting to measure his blood iron levels. It would likely come out at the top end of the 'normal' range, so most doctors wouldn't even see it as an issue.

But the real question is, how are the so-called normal ranges calculated by the medical profession? They simply measure the iron levels of a large sample of the overall male human population (different data sets are used for men and women), and then look at the range. All the numbers between the 5th and 95th percentile, which is where 90 per cent of the population falls, are deemed to be 'normal'. In other words, it is simply a confusion of terms where the population average is mistaken for normal.

But here is the problem: we know that one-third of American males die by age seventy, and nearly half by age seventy-nine.[8] So when looking at the 'normal' ranges, we are comparing ourselves to a range that includes 50 per cent mortality by age seventy-nine. How normal is that?

I don't know about you, but I want to compare myself to the 1 per cent of the male population that lives to be 100, not to the general male population. I want to see what the iron level ranges of those centenarians were when they were at my current age, and create a normal distribution of that information. I want my blood iron levels to be in the middle of *that* normal distribution. The same is true for any number of measures of health, whether it is Resting Heart Rate, blood pressure, liver function, lung capacity, Body Mass Index, you name it. I am not interested in the average for the general population. I am interested in the averages of people who have experienced long and healthy lifespans. And you should be too.

Toxic Shock Syndrome – the Infection That Affects Young Women

Every doctor I have spoken to regarding the role of excess iron in infections was sceptical at first, but had an open mind about the issue and was willing to consider that I might be right. But invariably, when I argue with them that women of menstruating age rarely get bacterial infections due to the low iron in their blood, they respond with the one major exception to the rule: toxic shock syndrome, which is caused by staph aureus and affects mainly young women.

Let us examine the facts. First of all, over 80 per cent of the incidences of this disease occur among women who use tampons during their menstrual period. Of the remaining 20 per cent, most have had surgery or some sort of surgical packing (such as packs inserted to stop nosebleeds).[9] The clues are self-evident from this profile of incidences. Clearly, something is happening that is exposing staph bacteria, which are part of the skin symbiote, to blood, through some kind of open wound, for a prolonged period.

On this point, it is important to note that the normal human circulatory system is a closed loop, where blood does not come into contact with the outside air. When this closed loop is disturbed and blood does come into contact with air, infections can arise at that site, especially because blood itself is full of iron and nutrients and bacteria love feeding on it. It is also true that around a quarter of the strains of staph aureus release an incredibly potent toxin called the toxic shock syndrome toxin (TSST-1), which is harmless when it is on the outside of the skin barrier, but can be deadly if it enters the blood stream. The most important thing to note is that in the case of toxic shock syndrome, the toxins are not produced by staph aureus multiplying in the blood stream. What actually happens is that the toxins are produced by the staph aureus at the site of the cut or open wound, which then enter the blood stream and cause the symptoms.

Clearly, blood iron levels have nothing to do with toxic shock syndrome, because the staph bacteria are multiplying in the blood. Given this, it is no surprise that this disease can affect anyone with an open and festering wound. In fact, calling this an infection is a misnomer. You cannot catch toxic shock syndrome from someone else. It is a non-infectious condition akin to poisoning; the fact that the poisons are produced at the site of an open wound by staph aureus does not make the staph aureus inherently evil.

Think of this toxin as similar to snake venom; you can drink snake venom all day as long as you don't have an ulcer in your body. Snake venom, like TSST-1, is not harmful unless it enters the blood stream.

How Taking Care of Your Teeth Reduces Heart Disease

Have you seen the ads for statins? Those supposedly miraculous drugs that lower cholesterol? It is my belief that statins will one day come to be seen as cigarettes are today—causing all kinds of illnesses with long-term use.

The single greatest killer of Americans is heart disease, killing one in three people. Of course, we all have to die of something or the other, so this statistic in itself may not tell us much. But 81 million Americans have some form of cardiovascular disease (CVD), according to the American Heart Association.[10]

The good news is that deaths from CVD have declined in the last decade, as more and better surgical treatments have become available. The problem is that surgical treatments for CVD are horribly expensive. In 2009 alone, the economic costs of CVD in the US were US$475 billion.[11] In the UK, the number for 2004 is £29 billion.[12] This is truly one disease where an ounce of prevention is worth several billion pounds of cure!

There are all kinds of myths and theories regarding heart

disease. The mainstream hypothesis is that high cholesterol, particularly high amounts of LDL cholesterol, is the root cause of heart disease. This hypothesis is so well established that the pharmaceutical industry makes billions on a class of drugs called statins, which lower measureable cholesterol in the blood stream. In 2006, the market for these drugs was US$18 billion in the US alone.

Let us look at exactly how this hypothesis works. Many studies have shown that people with naturally low cholesterol are less prone to heart disease than the general population. The science part of the cholesterol hypothesis ends here. From this data, someone decided that if you lower cholesterol in people who have naturally higher cholesterol through drugs, then you lower the incidence of heart disease too.

This is like saying brown-skinned people are less prone to skin cancer, so if Caucasians used tanning beds regularly their rate of skin cancer would go down too. In fact, the process of tanning would more likely *cause* them skin cancer!

The first question to ask is if artificially lowering cholesterol has any impact on heart disease. The answer is that it does not.

The second question is if the drugs themselves have huge side effects. The answer is that they do, from muscle weakness to impaired liver function to neurodegenerative illnesses.[13]

What does all this have to do with the human symbiote? Well, the symbiote has a big role to play in heart disease. The role is indirect, and works like this. Heart disease in reality is caused by chronically elevated levels of cortisol, a chemical released in the blood stream due to stress. The stress chemical, in turn, causes the body to increase the synthesis of cholesterol. The body does this because cholesterol is an antioxidant which counteracts the free radicals caused by stress.

Now let's think this through. The medical community wants us to take statins that lower the production of cholesterol, because increased levels of cholesterol are linked to heart disease. But cholesterol is the body's medicine against stress compounds, so why would we want to lower its levels? We should instead be getting to the root cause of stress and eliminating it.

There is so much evidence of the effects of stress that these are now part of the medical consensus.

Let's look at the biggest causes of cortisol release, which is the body's response to stress. Probably the number one cause is chronic inflammation of the teeth, or dental disease. Remember that the teeth and gums are the one place where the skin is continuously being broken due to chemicals released when food particles that are stuck between the teeth decompose. The mouth symbiote are just doing their job, which is breaking down the food particles. But a side effect is that harmful chemicals known as endotoxins are released when this breakdown takes place and these endotoxins can enter the blood stream and cause inflammation. The body fights this inflammation by releasing cortisol. This process can go on for years before you see damage in the form of heart disease, which is why dental disease has escaped attention in the past.

The healthy human mouth symbiote is made up of hundreds of species of bacteria that belong to a group called 'aerobic' bacteria, meaning that they need oxygen to survive.[14] These are normal inhabitants of the mouth symbiote, and are quite harmless. In fact, just like the skin symbiote, they are there to fight off any pathogens that enter your mouth by preventing them from establishing a presence. When you clean your teeth and gums, these bacteria re-establish themselves very quickly, so there is no harm to the mouth symbiote. But when you fail to clean your teeth and tongue and don't floss regularly, a layer of plaque forms on your teeth, which creates a barrier under which another class of bacteria called 'anaerobic' bacteria set up shop. These bacteria are far more likely to be harmful, because they release endotoxins that cause inflammation and stimulate the immune system to give a cortisol response.

The simple truth is that maintaining healthy gums and teeth is critical to preventing heart disease. Go to the dentist every six months and get your teeth professionally cleaned. Floss between your teeth every day, preferably at night before you go to sleep. Also, brush your tongue to remove the white coating of food underneath which anaerobic bacteria can establish themselves.

The Stunning Truth About Aspirin

There have been so many studies on the role of aspirin in reducing heart disease that there is a medical community consensus on this issue: a daily dose of aspirin can reduce your risk of heart disease by—wait for this—15 per cent!

There are two problems with this consensus. First, 15 per cent is not very high. Second, no one actually knows why aspirin reduces heart disease. Is it because it is a blood thinner, and thin blood is good for the heart? Does aspirin somehow slow down hardening of the arteries? No one knows.

But let me lay out a conjecture and challenge the medical community to disprove it. I have argued that excess iron increases cortisol and promotes plaque formation. This is the reason why men are more susceptible to heart disease than women in their thirties, forties and fifties. Post-menopause, women's iron levels gradually increase, and they catch up with men in the heart disease stakes in their seventies and eighties.

Enter the humble aspirin. Aspirin has been shown to increase microbleeds in the brain according to a well-accepted Dutch study.[15] But where else in the body are we bleeding when we take regular aspirin? We know that in larger doses, aspirin causes full-scale bleeding in the stomach and in the gastrointestinal tract. But what about microbleeds in the stomach at lower doses? I conjecture that the reason aspirin reduces the incidence of heart disease is because even in low doses it causes microbleeding in the stomach and gastrointestinal tract. Unlike the Dutch study, where MRI scanners were used to look at microbleeds in the brain, no one has yet looked at the stomach and intestinal tract of aspirin users using MRI scanners.

If my conjecture holds, the microbleeds leach out blood and hence iron from the body, and the lower iron levels in turn reduce plaque formation in arteries. If true, this conjecture could revolutionize our thinking on how to delay or reduce the incidence of heart disease. Don't bother with bleeding your gut by taking aspirin, because I will offer you a much safer and healthier prescription to get your iron levels down. Simply go to your nearest blood donation centre and donate a pint of blood. And do this every six months. We are back to bloodletting again.

We have so far discussed the role of iron as an essential nutrient for bacterial growth, both in the laboratory and in the human body. This is certainly true of many of the bacteria that are part of the symbiote, which is why maintaining the iron balance is so important in keeping bacterial infections in check. The reason I spent so much time on it is that bacteria that crave iron will gravitate towards animals that hoard it in their blood, including humans, and since this book is about enjoying a long and healthy life, we need to better manage the iron problem.

However, any attempt to reduce a subject as complex as human health and symbiote balance to a simple remedy is clearly not going to work in every instance. This is because evolution is a wonder of nature, and the complexity generated by the laws of evolution is massive. Iron balance is a good place to start looking when there are health problems, because iron is an essential nutrient and can easily be imbalanced, particularly if there are changes in our diet, exercise patterns or physiology.

But iron is not the only game in town, as far as bacteria are concerned. There are a few bacterial pathogens that have evolved to cause harm to humans even without using the excess iron stores in the human body. Probably the most famous of them from a human disease standpoint is Borrelia burgdorferi, which is the pathogen that causes Lyme disease.

B. burgdorferi uses manganese instead of iron as a growth medium. Manganese is present in both men and women, which is why Lyme disease affects both men and women equally. B. burgdorferi not only needs manganese to thrive, but because it competes with the human host for the body's stores of manganese, it causes all sorts of symptoms associated with manganese deficiency, which is a type of anaemia.

Iron, manganese, cobalt, nickel, copper and zinc are next to each other on the periodic table of element and they share many properties; for instance, they are all metallic. The first four are also paramagnetic elements that show magnetic properties. In chemical form, these six metals are essential micronutrients for the human body, and a balance of these chemicals is important to maintain good health. In fact, the chemical form of cobalt in the human body is none other than our friend vitamin B12, which is essential for the functioning of our brain and nervous system. Similarly, human bodies contain almost 10 mg manganese.

A healthy symbiote balance means a healthy immune system balance. When we take antibiotics and temporarily weaken the bacterial symbiote, the immune system can become hypersensitive, causing all kinds of autoimmune diseases. This alone is reason enough to minimize the use of antibiotics in public health today.

5

LEARNING TO LOVE OUR MICROBIAL FRIENDS

For people who are afraid of 'infectious bugs', here is something to chew on: some of the most pathogenic bacteria are very common members of the human symbiote, living on and inside our bodies, in benign coexistence with other bugs and our body cells. What this means is that an approach that involves trying to eliminate them from our environment altogether is a terrible idea, for two reasons. First, we don't know if these bacteria offer some compensating benefits, such as protecting the body from even worse pathogens. They probably do, because the body would not tolerate bugs that did not provide *some* benefit. Second, given how common these bacteria are and how great the human population, the probability that we can eliminate these bacteria from the entire human population is minuscule, even if it were desirable to attempt such a thing. The only approaches that are likely to work are those that address the root cause of why ordinary bacteria suddenly become pathogens.

There are two things to keep in mind in order to understand the process by which good bacteria turn into pathogens. The first is a genetic component, which means that somehow a benign or good bacterium in the human symbiote has mutated into a pathogenic strain. The second is quorum sensing, an odd behavioural trait that bacteria possess, which essentially turns normal bacteria into virulent beasts once a trigger is activated. Let us look at these things one at a time, because they offer some interesting clues to how different species of bacteria actually work to protect us from harm.

Until recently, it was a mystery why H. pylori, which has coexisted with humans for millennia, also has strains which cause ulcers. But recent advances in DNA sequencing have more or less solved this problem. If you look at the DNA of benign strains of H. pylori versus its more pathogenic, ulcer-causing evil twin, there is a distinct difference of about 6 per cent of the DNA. In fact, scientists are certain the pathogenic strain came from an entirely different bacterium, or even a virus! Now this kind of thing is not such a surprise, since bacteria are known to exchange DNA material with each other, and with viruses, all the time.

What this means is that at some point in recent history,

benign H. pylori acquired some pathogenic DNA from another bacteria or from a virus, and then formed an evil strain. In this, there are parallels to how cancers are formed in body cells. Cancer cells are normal cells that suddenly mutate into a virulent form, and they start multiplying, creating disease. So pathogenic strains of bacteria are like a cancer affecting a member of the bacterial symbiote.

The solution is clear from the identification of this problem: replace the pathogenic strain in the stomachs of ulcer sufferers with a benign one that does not cause ulcers. We can do this because we already know how to use antibiotics to wipe out the pathogenic H. pylori. But there is a second step that is not performed in modern medicine, at least in current thinking, which is to then repopulate the stomach with a good strain of H. pylori. It is this second part of the process that is required to restore the symbiote imbalance.

Sadly, we live in a world that treats all bugs as evil, including those bacteria that are card-carrying members of the human symbiote, and it has until quite recently been heretical to propose replacing a pathogenic bug with a benign strain.

There is also another huge problem, which is to do with economics. It is impossible to patent strains of bacteria that have been part of the symbiote for millennia. In fact, it was only in 1980 that a US Supreme Court ruling allowed genetically modified bacteria to be patented for the first time. But this ruling does not apply to strains of symbiote bacteria, which are co-adapted to humans and have been with us for a long time.

Faced with no profits from replacing pathogenic strains with benign ones, the pharmaceutical industry has fought the problem differently – by using antibiotics to wipe out H. pylori. This is the stomach symbiote equivalent of using a nuclear weapon on a city to weed out a few criminals in its midst, or treating a cancer with radiation that kills the entire organ where the cancer is growing.

Antibiotics are a quick and dirty solution, and one that makes a lot of money for pharmaceutical companies. The issue is that when medicine decided that H. pylori was the bad guy, no one knew what benefits it offered the human host, and whether wiping it out would create other problems.

Besides the issue of obesity and the long-term effects it has on human health, it turns out that H. pylori actually helps lower the production of stomach acid, thereby reducing the incidence of Gastroesophageal Reflux Disease (GERD).[1]

Eliminating H. pylori has also led to an epidemic of GERD in the West.

But Why, Oh Why, Do They Do This?

We have seen how bacteria can acquire virulent genes from other bacteria and even viruses and turn into pathogenic strains. A pathogenic strain of bacteria has two characteristics. One, it produces toxins that harm the human host. Two, the bacteria spread from person to person. The main question is, why do some strains of bacteria produce toxins? The basic hypothesis in this book is that bacteria, at least symbiote bacteria, have a vested interest in keeping the human host healthy. A dead host, after all, means a dead symbiote. A healthy host provides food and shelter to the symbiote, and natural evolution would tend to prefer a bacterial symbiote that coexists peacefully with the human body.

Producing toxins requires more energy than being a benign strain. This metabolic cost, as it is called, entails that, all other things remaining equal, a strain that produces toxins will be outcompeted by another strain that does not, because the strain with the lower metabolic load wins the evolution marathon.

The basic law that governs how bacteria evolve is the law of natural selection. Our understanding of natural selection has come a long way to the point where we can design specific treatments for bacterial infections that favour milder variants of bacteria rather than pathogenic ones.

For instance, we know that most bacteria are interested in the long-term well-being of the host. This is because if the human host is unable to move around (because the host is dead or otherwise incapacitated) the bacterium has less chances to spread from person-to-person. Any strain of bacteria or virus that inhibits its own transmission from host to host will die out versus a strain that does not. But if the bacteria or virus can jump easily from host to host, it becomes less interested in the well-being of each host, and natural selection will allow more of a chance for a pathogenic strain to develop. Put another way, both theory and research suggest that making it harder for a virus or bacteria to jump from host to host will lead to the prevalence of milder strains of the bacteria or virus.

To understand this dynamic better, let us look at an interesting bacterium called Corynebacterium diphtheriae. This bacterium lives harmlessly in the upper respiratory tract of healthy people, but it forms a dangerous strain when infected with a virus. The virus-infected bacteria produce a toxin which causes the deadly disease, diphtheria. The diphtheria toxin destroys the mucous membrane lining the throat, and in the process releases nutrients that the bacteria use to multiply. The irritation in the throat leads to a cough, which spreads the bacteria from person to person. These days, most people in the developed world are immunized against diphtheria.

The vaccine is a depleted version of the diphtheria toxin, which works by making the body's immune system aware of the toxin. When an immunized person is infected with pathogenic diphtheria, the toxin produced is immediately countered by the host immune system and it has no effect on the lining of the throat. This means that the pathogenic diphtheria is unable to release nutrients for the bacteria to multiply, and the pathogenic strain quickly dies out because producing the toxin carries a metabolic cost that no longer has any benefits. The result is that while Corynebacterium diphtheriae is still prevalent in the developed world, only the strain that does not carry the toxin has survived.

Acid Reflux: a Money Spinner for the Pharma Industry

Rob had a sore throat, so he went to the doctor. The doctor told him it was probably just a viral infection, there was no cure, and it would clear up on its own in a couple of days. Since the doctor did not give him any medicine, Rob did not feel that he had got his money's worth from the consultation. He pressed the doctor for prescription antibiotics. The doctor reluctantly wrote him a course of antibiotics, warning him that this had no effect on viral infections. Rob took the antibiotics, and his throat eventually cleared up. But there was a new problem. Suddenly Rob developed acid reflux, or GERD. He went back to the doctor, who put him on a permanent course of a pill to reduce the amount of acid produced by the stomach. Rob is still on this pill, because every time he misses his daily tablet, the acid reflux comes back.

Rob finally went to see a natural cure therapist, who recommended that Rob stop taking the pill, and instead go to a health food store and buy one sample each of all of the probiotic yogurts and supplements they had in stock. The therapist told

him to try them one at a time on an empty stomach, and to
see if any of them helped. Rob followed the therapist's advice.
It took about ten attempts before Rob noticed that the reflux
was gone. He is still not sure which of the yogurts did the trick,
but he isn't complaining!

It is extraordinary that so little has been studied about
the connection between GERD and antibiotics. Many, if
not all cases of GERD begin after a course of antibiotics has
been taken by a patient, so there must be some link. Why is
it that the stomach is suddenly producing too much acid?
It is pure conjecture at this point that there is an organism
in the symbiote that regulates stomach acid, but surely
we should do the research and find out more. But which
pharmaceutical company will bother with this research,
since there will be no patentable cure?

GERD basically means that your stomach is producing
too much acid, which then comes back up the esophagus
and into your mouth. This can be a chronic condition that is
quite dangerous because over time it can cause a condition
called Barrett's Esophagus, in which the stomach lining cells
start growing in your esophagus, and eventually lead to
esophageal cancer. The treatment for GERD is a tablet that
contains ranitidine, which has earned the pharmaceutical
industry about US$20 billion in profits during the patent
period of 1978–1995. Ranitidine basically regulates
the production of acid in the stomach, so that GERD
is controlled.

What is interesting is that within a decade of H. pylori being identified as a cause of ulcers and a massive campaign to kill it using antibiotics, there was an explosion of GERD in the Western world. Coincidence?

If this hypothesis turns out to be correct, the pharma industry is responsible for the antibiotics that kill a symbiote organism that regulates stomach acid, so that the organism can be replaced by a multi-billion-dollar money-spinning tablet.

Clap – the Exception to the Rule

I am not advocating banning antibiotics, I am merely suggesting that their use be restricted to essential purposes only. One of the most essential uses of antibiotics is for chlamydia or clap, a sexually transmitted disease. Rates of chlamydia are growing massively in the West; mainly because people are having sex at an earlier age, and also because they are having unprotected sex. Chlamydia is not directly life-threatening, but it can cause pelvic inflammatory disease and infertility. It is silent and destructive, because most of the time there are no visible symptoms, especially in women. Women can go through years of having it, all the time passing it on to their male partners and never realizing that they are infected. They only find out when they are trying to get pregnant and tests show that they are infertile because of pelvic inflammatory disease caused by chlamydia.

In Britain today, there is a campaign to test all sexually active young women for the disease. This is almost certainly the right approach; we cannot mandate morals but we can certainly mitigate the effects of careless sex on health.

Bacteria Need a Quorum to Misbehave

Let's look at the second cause of benign bacteria becoming pathogenic: quorum sensing.

Quorum sensing is mysterious because we don't understand how or why single-cell organisms like bacteria suddenly display a kind of 'mob madness', when they clearly don't have a brain that is guiding this group behaviour. We know, from the work of Bonnie Bassler on luminescent squid, how a critical mass of bacteria makes the bacteria glow together in unison.[2]

Luminescent or glowing bacteria are part of the squid symbiote. They live in a special sac inside the squid, and the squid uses the light from the bacteria to navigate the sea bed. As the sac is more or less transparent, the squid can shine a torch on its surroundings and find its way around. For a long time, scientists thought the squid itself produced a chemical that helped it glow, but we now know that this is not the case. It is the squid symbiote bacteria that do it. When there are enough of them, they undergo a process of quorum sensing and produce the chemical that makes them glow. In this case, the health of the symbiote is literally the difference between life and death for the squid; if the symbiote does not achieve quorum sensing, the squid cannot find its way to food, and it dies.

There are essentially two chemicals that bacteria use to achieve quorum sensing. One gives them a sense of how many of their fellow bacteria there are (which is a strain specific signal), and the second one gives them a sense of how many other species of bacteria there are in their immediate ecosystem. This quorum sensing triggers a particular response, usually a coordinated production of some chemical like a toxin, when a critical mass of same-strain bacterial cells is reached. This also happens if the quorum sensing tells the bacterium that other species of bacteria have reduced to a particular number. This process is similar to how the body uses hormones as chemical signals to communicate with human cells. So you can think of quorum chemical production as a kind of hormonal mechanism in the symbiote.

Bonnie Bassler is researching how we can use quorum sensing to develop better antibiotics. Essentially, her premise is that if we block the quorum sensing chemical, the bacteria do not go through the virulent phase and produce toxins, therefore infection is stopped in its tracks. But this is not a convincing argument. Even if blocking quorum sensing stops bacteria from becoming virulent, it does not treat the underlying cause of why the bacteria multiplied to critical mass in the first place. Was it the availability of excess iron, a weakness in the immune system, or a deficiency in minerals that caused a reduction in the number of symbiote species on the body? It can be any of these things, and blocking quorum sensing may stop the virulence of the particular strain of bacteria, but it will not stop a different strain of bacteria from multiplying and becoming virulent. And this approach will certainly not treat the underlying cause, which may end up being more dangerous for the body anyway (for instance, we know that the underlying cause is definitely more dangerous if it is an iron imbalance).

A far better approach would be to try and change the expression of the virulence. We know that different strains of, say, staph bacteria are implicated in different kinds of diseases when they undergo quorum sensing. One strain causes boils. Another can cause a condition known as necrotizing fasciitis, or flesh-eating bacteria. But what if we created a strain of staph which, when undergoing quorum sensing, simply shows the luminescent properties of the bacterium? If you have an excess amount of this strain of staph, your skin would simply light up like a glow worm, and you could then go to the doctor and see what is causing this excess production of staph.

Keep Out of Hospitals

In nineteenth-century Vienna, women in labour admitted to hospitals would beg to go out onto the street to give birth, rather than have their babies delivered by a doctor in the hospital. It was widely known that the chance of death by infection in hospital deliveries was very high for both mother and child. The mortality rate for mothers delivering a baby in Vienna hospitals was 1 in 10, whereas the rate outside the hospital was minuscule. This was at a time before people knew that bacteria can cause infections, and doctors scrubbing hands before performing surgery was unheard of. Doctors routinely performed autopsies on bodies and went straight into delivery rooms to assist in births, and they would be insulted if you asked them to wash their hands!

Thankfully, we now know the importance of sterilizing procedures in any surgical or invasive procedures, including childbirth. But as I have mentioned earlier in this book, hospitals remain a serious source of infection. A study in Britain shows that nearly 8 per cent of hospital patients acquired infections while in hospital, and nearly 20 per cent of patients reported symptoms of hospital-acquired infections after being discharged from hospital.[3] These are stunning numbers, given that bacterial infections are so rare in the Western world, especially outside the hospital.

The point is that hospitals are a place where surgeries and other invasive procedures are performed. An invasive procedure by definition involves getting past not only the skin symbiote, but the skin itself. Since hospitals are aware of the threat of infections, they tend to be over-cautious in scrubbing and cleaning, ensuring that only the hardiest bacteria survive. Add to this the fact that the blood stream is full of nutrients that bacteria love and hospitals are the most likely place where bad bugs come in contact with the blood stream, and the result is bad news.

There is no question that areas where surgical procedures are performed must be kept sterile. Hospitals and doctors should also ensure that antibiotics are not misused or prescribed unnecessarily. But if history is any guide, the prognosis is not encouraging in this respect.

The real issue is that we still do not understand the biology of indoor environments. We know by now that the outdoors is generally a healthy place, full of natural bacteria that are quite benign to the human interloper. But the indoor environments that we spend most of our time in are not at all understood. There are some places that seem designed to make you ill, such as moldy basements, damp stairwells, windowless rooms. To this category one could add hospitals, judging by the incidence of hospital-acquired infections in the modern world. What is astonishing is that in the olden times, when hospitals were built with high ceilings, lots of natural light and huge windows, people seemed to get better in a hospital. These days, with all the air-conditioning and modern technology we use, people seem to get sicker in a hospital! Yes, there could be a number of reasons for this (such as the fact that people are much older these days when they go for a hospital procedure), but there is research going on that shows that opening windows and letting in natural air can reduce hospital acquired infections and improve the health of patients. Rebecca Green at the University of Oregon is doing cutting-edge research that shows how indoor air quality, particularly in hospitals, has a huge impact on health.[4]

The reasons for this are not yet clear, but there is strong conjecture at this point that it has to do with the lack of symbiote balance in a closed environment. If there aren't hundreds of bacterial species competing for superiority and checking each other, chances are that a pathogenic species can jump from one patient and spread throughout the ward. In time, hospitals will be designed better. In the meantime, as consumers, we should only go to the hospital as a last resort. Unless you are having a major procedure done or giving birth, stay away from hospitals!

The Difficulty of Accepting a Poo Donation

One day, we will all get over our collective fear of bacteria and germs, and one day the scam artists who have been selling disinfectants and antibiotics will fade away in human history.

Meanwhile, let me hasten this vision by telling you about an amazing treatment for a difficult chronic condition. There is a bacterium called Clostridium difficile that lives in the guts of most people, and it is a normal member of the human symbiote. In countries where antibiotic use is prevalent, clostridium occasionally turns into a dangerous pathogen. Essentially, it is kept in check in the gut by the trillions of other bacteria that live there. When you use an antibiotic, large swathes of your gut bacteria are wiped out. Clostridium is a hardy, antibiotic-resistant bacterium that tends to survive this nuclear attack on the gut, so in the aftermath of antibiotic use you could end up with a massive overgrowth of clostridium in the gut. When the concentration of clostridium increases beyond a certain point, certain strains of it undergo quorum sensing and start producing toxins. This can cause diarrhoea, ulcerative colitis, bloating and flu-like symptoms. There are few better arguments in favour of a balanced ecosystem in the human body than a clostridium overgrowth infection.

Besides antibiotic use, the second main cause of clostridium overgrowth infections is the use of acid reflux medication, like proton-pump inhibitors or stomach acid inhibitors.[5] This is because lowering stomach acid levels makes for a more hospitable environment for clostridium. You will recall that acid reflux is itself a disease caused by destroying H. pylori bacteria, so now we have a cascade of disease upon disease caused by medication.

In other words, clostridium is a deadly reminder to humans that the war on bacteria cannot be won, and indeed, should not be fought in the first place.

So is there a solution to the deadly clostridium overgrowth infection? Yes, there is, and a rather unusual one at that.

It turns out that clostridium infections can be cured by

something called faecal enema. The process is simple, if a little gross. You take some excrement from a spouse or close relative, mix it with saline solution, and pump it directly into your rectum like an enema. The idea is to repopulate your gut with friendly bacteria, which will keep the clostridium in check.[6]

Doctors treat clostridium overgrowth infections with vancomycin, a next-generation antibiotic that can kill many strains of clostridium, although it is only a matter of time before clostridium becomes immune to it. Faecal enemas are simple, can be done at home and don't cost a thing. Unlike vancomycin, which simply kills clostridium, leaving your body bare for the next lot of random bacteria to colonize, a faecal enema will almost certainly cure the illness by restoring your body's natural bacteria. If the faeces are taken from a close relative, chances of any other pathogens coming into your gut are remote. But today, most gastroenterologists have not even heard of this cure, and the ones that have are queasy about it, even though it works.

The idea of faecal donations goes well beyond curing clostridium overgrowth infections. I believe this is just the beginning. We know, for example, that obese people have a different gut composition of bacteria from skinny people. The problem always has been that it is difficult to alter the gut composition of bacteria. Whatever probiotics you take have to survive the intense environment of the stomach acid before they can enter the gut. Even then, there is little possibility that they can displace the existing bacterial balance. But faecal enemas have amazing potential. I can envision a situation where an obese person is initially given a combination of broad spectrum antibiotics to wipe their gut clean, and then given a faecal enema from a close relative who happens to be skinny. This would give them a different, presumably healthier, bacterial balance. Would this help them lose weight? Intriguing studies into mice show that this is possible. Scientists have shown that fat mice lose weight when their gut microbes are replaced with gut microbes from skinny mice.[7] A faecal enema could be just the mechanism to do this, because you don't have to negotiate the harsh conditions of the stomach to get this new ecosystem to take hold in the gut.

The possibilities are endless. Vitamin deficiency? We use targeted gut microbes that produce vitamins and send them up the same channel, where they can colonize your gut and start producing vitamins.

It All Starts on the Farm

Agribusiness is one of the largest industries in the world. As with every business, there is a specific problem (in this case, the need to feed 7 billion humans) that is addressed by competitive market forces with ruthless efficiency. The efficiency of agribusiness is so great that only the biggest corporate farms in the world are profitable. The majority of small farmers are either heavily subsidized by governments, or eke out a marginal existence in countries where governments are unable to provide decent handouts. At the same time, the beneficiary of this efficiency has been the consumer, who now has an incredible abundance of food available at dirt-cheap prices.

Some of you may quibble with this, and you may even feel that grocery prices are increasing, but a quick historical perspective is in order. For instance, every family in Ireland a hundred years ago that could had a kitchen garden where they grew vegetables, including potatoes. It took typically one month of manual labour to tend to this garden, with a resulting yield of, say, ten kilos of potatoes. Today in London you can buy a ten-kilo bag of potatoes for five pounds, which is about forty-five minutes of work at the minimum wage. Comparing like-for-like, the price of potatoes has fallen from thirty days of manual labour to forty-five minutes. I would certainly call that a major consumer benefit of agribusiness! Now instead of eating potatoes you may choose to buy meat or ready meals or eat in a restaurant, all of which were extremely scarce options in nineteenth-century Ireland, but you must compare potatoes with potatoes to see how much better off you are as a consumer today.

What does this have to do with the human symbiote? As it turns out, a lot. Agribusiness has long evolved from a simple model of meeting the calorific needs of 7 billion humans. Today, the majority of crops grown go into supplying the livestock industry, which did not exist 200 years ago. This industry exists to serve the increasing human demand for meat and dairy products. For example, there are ten sheep in New Zealand for every human being, so it is not surprising that the majority of New Zealand's exports are agriculture and livestock related. But the livestock industry has also been on a ruthless drive to improve efficiency, and a significant part of this effort has been to turn farms essentially into factories specializing in growing single genotypes within the same species of chicken, cattle, etc. and removing any biodiversity that has historically enabled animals to survive pathogen attacks. The price of this is the widespread use of antibiotics to keep pathogens at bay, because farm animals are very vulnerable to infection. It has long been known that antibiotics not only keep these monoculture farm animals healthy, but in low and continuous doses they also enable them to grow faster and larger, thus increasing profits. In 1950, it took eighty-four days to produce a five-pound chicken, today it takes just forty-five days![8] This is the power of antibiotics, but there is a cost too.

Given the production gains, antibiotics have been produced in industrial quantities and fed to livestock. In the United States, nearly 70 per cent of the total antibiotic use is in agriculture, that too for non-therapeutic reasons.[9] The result of this is predictable. The animal symbiote has fought back in the only way it knows – natural selection. Two things have happened. First, over time the antibiotics have become less effective as the microbes developed drug resistance. Second, drug-resistant bacteria have emerged from farms and spread through the general population. According to the Centers for Disease Control, about 2 million people in the US develop drug-resistant bacterial infections each year, and 90,000 die of these infections. The farm factories have fought back, not only by denying any responsibility for the effects of drug-resistant bacteria, but by asking for even more potent antibiotics to be approved for use in cattle feed.

Let us think for a moment about the conflict between ecological balance and economics. Someone once described the entire field of economics in four words: 'People respond to incentives'. How often we forget this simple truth!

The humble cow is the battleground for all the mistakes that have ever been made in farm policy worldwide. In the beginning, there was the cow, which evolved to eat grass. But grass evolved into a form that made it increasingly difficult to digest, and it got to a point where the natural enzymes required to digest grass became greater than the metabolic capabilities of the grass-eating cow. But the cow evolved too, this time in a novel way. It developed a larger stomach sectioned into four distinct regions, and in one of these sections grew cow symbiote bacteria strong enough to digest the thickest and toughest of grasses. This is pretty much what the modern cow is.

The farm factories waded into this quagmire. They

replaced grass with protein meal, and added antibiotics to the meal to make the cow grow faster. In the US, they added meat renderings to the cow diet, essentially turning a ruminant (meaning multiple-stomached) vegetarian into a carnivore. This worked for a while, and then the animals started getting sick with foot-and-mouth disease, mad cow disease and a number of antibiotic resistant infections, and now antibiotic resistance has found its way into human populations too. According to the World Health Organization, resistant strains of four bacteria that affect humans have now been transmitted to people from animals – E. coli, salmonella, campylobacter and enterococci. These bacteria are resistant not only to the antibiotics used on animals, but to those used to fight serious illness in humans.

Today, almost all staph bacteria are resistant to penicillin and streptomycin, and hospital-acquired staph infections are resistant to even advanced antibiotics like meticillin and vancomycin.

And this is where we find ourselves now.

What Can We Do About It?

The first step is to ban all non-therapeutic uses of antibiotics. Yes, this will ultimately cause the cost of meat to go up, to double or even more. But consider this: right now in the US, people spend 5 per cent of their disposable income on food at home, compared with around 10 per cent in 1970.[10] All we need to do is to roll the food budget of the average consumer back to 1970 levels, in exchange for improvements in public health that can be measured in multiples of the cost. The simple fact is that meat production takes a terrible toll on the ecosystem and human health, which is out of proportion with the benefits it delivers to consumers. Ninety per cent of food grains are used to grow factory animals; 87 per cent of all fresh water is used to grow the food grains; factory animals produce vast quantities of greenhouse gases. The list goes on and on. The solution is for public policy to reflect these costs better in the production of meat. Stop subsidizing animal feed, and move the subsidies over to help farmers grow meat without antibiotics. If this results in less meat being produced, higher meat prices and consequently a drop in meat consumption, we will get an additional bonus in the form of lower heart disease rates too! We can all do with eating less meat, and the only way to achieve this is to make it more of a luxury item. In no way am I advocating banning meat or anything as ridiculous as that, I am merely advocating using the pricing mechanism to make meat more of an occasional treat, instead of the state of excess consumption that we see today because of factory farming.

While the interest groups fight this war over the next few decades, let us come back to your health, and what we can do about it as individual consumers. First, do not buy any produce or meat or dairy from farms that use antibiotics.

Pay more for food and support small community farms. Food that comes from a balanced symbiote is more likely to promote a healthy and balanced human symbiote. If you can afford it, buy artisanal products from small farms. Remember that higher prices paid for food translates into increased farm incomes, which means that farmers are less likely to cut corners when growing food. Above all, eat less meat, and when you do buy it, pay particular attention to where it comes from and how it is grown. Walk right past the meat section in the supermarket, and go to the local organic butcher.

6

HARNESSING BACTERIA TO HELP US

ॐ

The virulence of a bacterium can be explained very easily by the amount of time it takes to multiply. Bacteria like E. coli and S. aureus multiply every twenty minutes, which makes them extremely virulent. Twenty minutes might seem like a long time for a microbe, but let us think this through. If you started with a single S. aureus bacterial cell, in twenty minutes you would have two cells, and in an hour you would have only eight cells. But here comes the crazy math: in six hours, you have 262,000 bacterial cells, in twelve hours, 68 billion cells, and in twenty-four hours, the number of bacteria is four followed by twenty-one zeroes!

Of course, in reality this kind of exponential growth does not occur inside the human body for long. For one thing, the bacteria need vast resources to multiply in this fashion, such as limitless food and iron. Also, the body starts fighting back with an immune response that kills bacteria by the billions.

Bakers are familiar with the exponential growth of yeast cells. When yeast and sugar are added to dough, it starts to rise because the yeast consume the sugar and start multiplying. As part of the multiplication, they eat the sugar and convert it into alcohol and carbon dioxide gas, and it is this gas that causes the dough to rise. Left unchecked, the dough would rise into a big puff that would bake into a fluffy and unpalatable ball of bread. The baker therefore adds a little salt to the dough, which inhibits the growth of the yeast, and the result is bread of the right consistency.

In the human body, bacterial growth works in a similar manner. The nutrients available for bacteria are ingested by us, but at the same time, we also have various bacterial growth inhibitors that control this process of exponential growth. These inhibitors can be other bacteria, our immune system, or a simple limit in the number of nutrients available to the bacteria. This is the reason why there is a symbiote balance in the body.

Exponential growth of bacterial cells also explains why they can spread so easily from person to person. There are billions of bacterial cells on our skin, in our mouths and noses, and on every surface around us. The answer is not to try and limit our senses of smell, touch and taste in order to avoid harmful strains of bacteria, because that would be futile. The real answer is to maintain a healthy symbiote balance in our body, so that harmful strains are unable to take root.

But not all bacteria multiply every twenty minutes. There are plenty of bacteria that have a much lower rate of multiplication, and this means they spread less quickly from one person to another. These bacteria spend a lot of their resources on building defences to evade the host immune system, and the trade-off is that they grow very slowly. Mycobacterium tuberculae is an example of a slow-growing bacteria, replicating only once every twenty hours.

The World of Bio- and Genetic Engineering

There are thousands of small biotechnology companies trying to make a business out of improving health. Consider Company A. The basic premise behind this company is simple: the human mouth symbiote contains a bacterium called Streptococcus mutans, which lives on our teeth. S. mutans munches on the remnants of the food that we eat, and essentially acts as a cleaning agent. The problem is that it then produces a waste product, lactic acid, which causes tooth decay by wearing down our teeth enamel over time.

Company A has a very interesting solution to this problem. At first, they tried to create a strain of S. mutans that did not produce lactic acid. But this strain did not live long, because it could not rid itself of the waste products from its own cells. Next, the company replaced the gene responsible in S. mutans for producing lactic acid with one that produces alcohol. The result is a strain of S. mutans that not only does not cause tooth decay, but actually acts as a mild mouth freshener! It is a beautiful tale, but I would urge caution. There are thousands of species of bacteria that live in our mouths. It is an elegant feat of genetic engineering to mess with one of them and turn it from foe to friend, but what are the possible unintended consequences? Do we know if some of that lactic acid produced by S. mutans helps sustain other bacterial species that provide an as yet unknown benefit? Do we know that the mild alcohol that the new strain of S. mutans produces will not change the eco-balance in our mouths and let some previously incompatible pathogen take root?

You may be surprised to learn that even though bioengineering appears to be a relatively new field, history is full of failed bioengineering experiments. A famous example of bioengineering that went seriously wrong is that of the cane toad, a poisonous predator that is native to the Americas. This creature was released on islands all over the world, including Australia, in the early part of the twentieth century, as a form of pest control. The idea was that it would prey on beetles and rats and protect crops. In Australia, which is an island continent with a unique ecosystem, the cane toad has caused devastation, reducing the biodiversity of the continent by a significant amount. And yet this is the sort of thing that biotechnology firms are talking about on a microbial scale when they mess about with living ecosystems such as the one in our mouths.

When is bioengineering acceptable? I would argue that the best example of good bioengineering thus far is in the commercial production of insulin. Insulin is a hormone that is produced in our bodies by the pancreas. But people with Type 1 diabetes cannot produce insulin, and without injecting commercially produced insulin, they would die. Up until the 1920s, this meant that children's hospital wards were full of children dying from juvenile diabetes. Although animal extract insulin began to save these lives starting in 1922, it was only in 1978 that the first synthetic insulin was produced using bioengineering, and Type 1 diabetes finally became a manageable chronic condition.

The process of making synthetic insulin is amazing. It all boils down to a part of the bacterial cell called the plasmid. A plasmid is simply a type of DNA present in bacteria that can replicate itself but cannot survive outside the bacterial cell. Plasmids are important because they contain the genes that help bacteria survive. For instance, a gene that produces a chemical which in turn provides resistance to antibiotics might be coded in a plasmid that is inside a bacterium.

A gene that produces a toxin could also very well be in a plasmid, and this can turn a benign strain of bacteria into a pathogenic one. When bacteria exchange genetic material with each other, it is often the plasmids that are acquiring new genes through a process called 'horizontal transfer'.

In 1978, scientists figured out a way to take our faecal friend E. coli bacteria, which is the single most common bacterium found in and around human habitation, and alter it in the lab. They injected a gene into its plasmid that produces insulin. Since E. coli bacteria divide every twenty minutes, in a fairly short time they ended up with large quantities of synthetic insulin. Problem solved.

Producing a chemical compound synthetically by using bacteria is a good idea, because the risk of unintended consequences is minimal. These chemicals are produced in sealed vats, and the strain of bacteria used for the purpose cannot survive outside the lab. This is very different from altering the ecological balance of the human mouth or the digestive tract in entire populations, which can result in unforeseen consequences.

I am not against progress, and in principle I think progress involves bettering the gifts that nature and evolution have given us. As we have discussed elsewhere in this book, evolution is not perfect. It can always be improved upon. Humans have moved away from the simple evolutionary aim of propagation of the species, and have developed further priorities such as providing ourselves with good health and high quality of life well into old age. But at the same time, lessons from history and bioengineering cannot be ignored. The lesson is simple – tread lightly.

Obesity, Oxidative Stress and the Symbiote

Let's move on from the benefits of exercise and consider the role of obesity in increasing oxidative stress. Obesity is basically the presence of adipose fat tissue in the body, it is not simply a question of body weight. If a person has lots of muscle and little adipose fat, they are not obese. There are a number of studies that show that an excess of adipose fat is linked to higher oxidative stress, one of these shows that the fat itself produces and releases harmful chemicals called free radicals.[1] In particular, fat around the abdomen is indicative of oxidative stress. Oxidative stress causes insulin resistance and a much higher risk of heart disease and diabetes; collectively these symptoms are known as Metabolic Syndrome (MetS).

So what causes fat build-up around the abdomen and obesity in general? This is where we pierce the wall between the cellular universe and the stomach and gut. Obese people have different gut bacteria from people of normal weight. Specifically, obese people have a higher proportion of firmicutes than bacteroidetes.[2] The question until recently was, which is the cause and which one the effect? Does a higher proportion of firmicutes cause obesity, or does obesity lead to a higher proportion of firmicutes? It appears the answer is both. When obese mice have their gut flora altered to increase bacteriodetes and reduce firmicutes, they drop weight quickly. But the weight does not stay off in the absence of dietary changes that caused the mice to become obese in the first place. So the mechanism seems to be this – a high fat diet causes firmicutes to multiply and leads to obesity, which then sustains the firmicutes. It is a vicious cycle. But if the gut bacteria are altered along with dietary changes, not only do you have a very quick reduction of body weight but also a sustainable reduction. There we have it – the symbiote balance has a major role to play in obesity and the oxidative stress that it causes, but we are ultimately responsible for the symbiote balance because of the diet we choose to eat.

What is the answer? Eat less frequent meals (forget about the six small meals a day nonsense!), eat well, start lunch and dinner with a salad so that you fill up with healthy food, and then eat whatever else strikes your fancy as long as it is a varied diet. Stop a few bites before you are completely full.

The Difference between Men and Women: a Symbiote's View

There is plenty of evidence that male and female health issues are different. The composition of the symbiote in men and women is broadly similar, but there are significant differences. Since there are physical, hormonal and physiological differences between men and women, it is only natural that there are also symbiote differences. Researchers at the University of Zurich recently found that men and women are prone to different kinds of illnesses when travelling.[3] Specifically, men are more prone to malaria and other so-called vector- and parasite-borne illnesses, but women are more prone to irritable bowel syndrome (which is an autoimmune illness), diarrhoea and urinary tract infections (which are caused by E. coli).

What are the possible explanations for these disparities? How and why are the male and female symbiote and physiological profiles so different that they cause even men and women to catch different diseases?

There are clearly many factors. For instance, the susceptibility in women to urinary tract infections is mainly physiological; they have shorter urinary tracts, and the shorter physical distance between their anal and urinary tract openings means that E.coli from their anus can more easily get into their urinary tract and cause infection.

It is also true that women travellers tend to cover up more of their skin, and this undoubtedly plays a role in their getting fewer mosquito and tick bites, and fewer infections. But these explanations are only part of the story. The real truth lies in something more fundamental.

Gene, Gene, the Sequencing Machine

'Papa, bhai is eating dirt in the garden. Ewww!' My son came running into the kitchen, his voice shaking me out of a mid-day snooze. I cast a groggy eye outside, and there was our toddler in the sunshine, apparently munching on something. I went to take a closer look, and sure enough, he had put some dirt into his mouth and was in the process of spitting it out. Things were pretty much under control, I could tell. Our little one was just exploring his surroundings, figuring out what is edible and what isn't. No need to panic.

As I saw my sons playing in the garden, just looking at them made me think about the wonder that is life; each one embodying half my genes, and half their mother's.

Our body's genes are mostly what we inherit from our parents. These genes also hold the information to build and maintain our body's cells. Every living organism has these genes, including the bacteria that live on our body.

There is a reason the term gene pool became popular. If you are picturing a vast swimming pool where genes are like water molecules, moving around and coming into contact with each other all the time, you would not be far from what happens in the great pool of life. At the cellular level, living organisms are exchanging genes with one another all the time, like in a gigantic swap meet. The reason they do this is simple – survival. The natural environment is changing all the time, and so is the ecosystem, as species adapt, evolve or die out. Random exchanges of genes are likely to result in a mutation that will confer some advantage in surviving and fitting into a certain environment. This is how single-cellular organisms were able to form multi-cellular organisms in the first place – by exchanging genes and specializing in one specific task in a larger collective.

For the most part, complex multi-cellular organisms like humans exchange genes through sexual reproduction. Hence my sons have half my genes and half my wife's genes, mixed together and shuffled to express the individual traits that we both recognize, as well as other traits that came from our ancestors. This is called vertical gene transfer.

Single-cellular organisms, like bacteria and viruses, do not reproduce sexually. When they reproduce, the vertical gene transfer only results in clones that have exactly the same genes as their parent cells. So how do these organisms exchange genes?

It turns out there is a far simpler process of exchanging genes than sexual reproduction. Single-celled organisms can transfer individual genes to each other, without any reproduction involved, in a process called horizontal gene transfer (HGT).

HGT happens mainly in one of three ways. The first is called Transformation, when genetic material is introduced into a bacterial cell, which results in a different bacterial strain. This process occurs naturally and randomly, as when the stomach bug H. pylori develops a nasty strain that causes stomach ulcers. Scientists have figured out how to artificially recreate the process of Transformation, and today it is used all the time in genetic engineering, like in the production of insulin, discussed earlier. The second way is Transduction, where a virus infects a bacterial cell and introduces new genetic material into it. The third is simply exchanging material via cell-to-cell contact.

Scientists only discovered HGT in 1959, but it is clear that it is one of the guiding elements of life and a key mechanism in evolution.[4] It is how single-cellular organisms become multi-cellular ones, and it should come as no surprise that HGT is so common among single-celled organisms; humans and other species would never have evolved without it.

The possibility of HGT among complex multi-cellular organisms is one of the main arguments against genetic modification of crops, because there is a danger that transgenic traits that have been created in crops and animals by human technology will jump from one species to another in the wild, with unpredictable consequences. On the positive side, if we discover a safe way to use HGT in humans, a revolutionary form of medicine called gene therapy, where faulty genes are replaced by better ones, would become possible.

Modern DNA sequencing is giving us some amazing information on our genes. There are 30,000 human genes at work in your body. But there are also some 3 million bacterial genes that make up your bacterial symbiote, and they are also at work in and on your body all the time.

In fact, our relationship with bacteria is even more intimate. Every single cell in our body contains components called mitochondria, which are ancient bacterial cells.

Mitochondria are the engines of the living cell; they are responsible for converting oxygen and food into energy. Latest research shows that the common ancestor of all animals and plants is actually a single cell that fused with a mitochondrion bacterium to form a super-cell.[5] Given this, it is not surprising that as we became multi-cellular organisms, we retained deep connections with our bacterial cousins.

How much of our health is determined by our genes, and how much by our environment? Are we products of nature or nurture? This is the great health debate of our time.

We inherit our initial bacterial symbiote from our parents and our initial dietary habits too. But over time, our interaction with our natural environment alters the bacterial symbiote balance that we inherited from our parents. It is the same with our diet, which tends to be the same as our parents to begin with, but changes over time.

If there is a single common enemy that the human ecosystem has, it is viruses. A hundred times smaller than bacterial cells, many viruses are truly nasty pathogens from a human standpoint, and they infect not only humans but also plants, bacteria, fungi and archaea (a type of microorganism that has no known interaction with humans). They have been around since the beginning of life, and they are more numerous than any other organism on our planet.

Viruses are neither alive nor dead and are able to survive indefinitely, but can only reproduce inside living cells.

A hundredth the size of bacteria, a virus cannot be seen under a conventional microscope. When you consider the devastation that viruses have wreaked and continue to wreak on humanity, you would be forgiven for wondering what their purpose in evolution is.

In fact, viruses do serve a very important evolutionary purpose: they are the most important vehicle for HGT. HGT increases the genetic diversity of a species and allows life to survive environmental changes.

There are millions of viruses, and the vast majority is completely harmless to humans. But the ones that are dangerous, such as HIV, smallpox or influenza, are truly fearsome from a public health standpoint.

On a daily basis, the viruses that irritate most of us are the type known as rhinoviruses, which cause the common cold. At any given time, we are infected with up to a dozen rhinoviruses. It is not possible to completely eliminate colds from our everyday lives, but there are steps we can take to minimize them. The first thing to understand is that the common cold virus thrives when certain parts of our body are exposed to cold temperatures for a period of time. The parts of our body that are the most vulnerable are the ears and throat. In cold weather, the majority of our body heat is lost via our earlobes. There is an old wives' tale in England that sticking your fingers in your ears can soothe a sore throat. This is partly true; the nerves in the ear are linked to the nerves in the throat, but more importantly, a pair of ear muffs in cold weather can do wonders to reduce the incidence of the common cold.

Another way to prevent the common cold is to always breathe with your nose and not with your mouth. You would think that this is an obvious statement, but it is remarkable how much people tend to breathe with their mouths. A class of yogic breathing would do wonders for most people in terms of reducing their susceptibility to colds. The nose is well-designed for breathing; it has specialized hairs to filter dust and a passageway that warms the air on its way to the lungs; it has immune cells in the lining waiting to pounce on any pathogen that comes through the air. The throat, on the other hand, has none of these things. The mucous membrane that lines it is prone to drying up, and a dry throat allows viruses to take hold quite easily.

A third way to ward off colds and other common viruses is to lower stress. I am talking about lowering the base levels of our old nemesis, cortisol, which is a glucosteroid that acts like an immune suppressant in the human body. Do you remember the last time you were sleep-deprived or otherwise stressed out, and you came down with a cold? Or maybe a cold sore broke out in your mouth or on your lips? There is a direct connection between elevated stress, which elevates cortisol, leading to colds and cold sores.

One can argue that the smallpox virus has shaped the course of human history more than any other pathogen. It is hard to imagine this today; smallpox was eliminated from the planet over thirty years ago, and only survives in some laboratories in strictly controlled conditions. Yet it killed millions of humans in the past.

In places like North and South America, where the natives had no resistance and the European conquerors figured out that entire communities could be wiped out by introducing smallpox, the virus became a biological weapon and a tool of genocide.

The reason public health authorities are terrified of viruses is four-fold. One, they spread rapidly, either through the air or through contact. Two, most viruses have no cure as such, and once they infect the human host the illness takes its own course. Three, they evolve, and developing vaccines is a process that is always one step behind this viral mutation. The fourth reason is probably the scariest of all – HGT, which is the same tool that provides living organisms with genetic diversity. Through this process, some viruses are capable of passing genetic material from one organism to another.

Most viruses are not members of the human symbiote; they are competing organisms in the planetary symbiote, and their evolutionary strategy does not depend on the survival of the human race, but rather on their sheer ability to mutate and adapt to living inside any living host, including bacterial cells. This is ultimately why we can never make friends with viruses.

An example of the deadliness of viruses is the fate of Tasmanian devils. Confined to the island of Tasmania, off the coast of Australia, Tasmanian devils are a species of mammal that are systematically being wiped out by a virus that spreads among them through physical contact. The virus causes ulcers on their face which do not heal, and the lesions increase in size until the animal dies. Given the lack of genetic diversity among these small island-based mammals, it is likely that the species will become extinct.

From a group survival standpoint, it is unlikely that a single virus is capable of wiping out humanity, because over thousands of years we have acquired enough genetic diversity in the human race, and our population is over 7 billion strong, spread out across the globe. This means that a portion of us is always immune to whatever virus nature can throw at us. But this is small comfort to public health officials; their job is to protect every single human from viruses, and not merely to statistically ensure the survival of the overall human race. This job is exceedingly difficult, and there is always a chance that a virus like SARS or Ebola can evolve into a form that could wipe out a large part of the human population.

Research on viruses is ongoing, but there is so much that science does not understand. The problem is that technological advance and the profit motive will likely get far ahead of understanding the full consequences of messing around with viruses. This has already happened in certain places in the former Soviet Union.

Some viruses, known as phages, can be destructive to bacteria. With this in mind, scientists in the former Soviet Union did decades of research into whether targeted viruses can be used in place of antibiotics to treat bacterial illnesses. The results of that research were mixed, but what is truly scary is the presumption that you can control a virus and make it do your bidding. I have cautioned against the overuse of antibiotics elsewhere in this book, but one good thing about antibiotics is that being chemical compounds, they are not self-replicating organisms. While bacteria do eventually become resistant to them, you will never see a situation where an antibiotic escapes the laboratory and turns into a pathogen.

Viruses are different. They are self-replicating organisms and extremely hard to control. Yes, it is possible to develop a viral strain that can kill, say, a pathogenic strain of a bacterium that is normally a part of the human symbiote. But will this virus differentiate between good and bad strains of the bacteria? Unlikely. The major issue with letting loose genetically engineered life on the world is that all forms of life might evolve. There is no way to anticipate in which direction it will evolve, or to have confidence that today's benign virus will remain harmless. Just as it pays never to forget that every mass-murderer in history was once a cute baby, we should recognize the limits of our ability to tinker with nature. This is not an indictment against science, merely a warning that we should be extremely careful.

I am not entirely against phage research. It is possible that certain bacterial illnesses can be cured by phages, and being a targeted therapy it might be a better approach than using so-called broad spectrum antibiotics, in terms of its impact on the human symbiote. In fact, we already use viruses in human health; many vaccines, including the one for chicken pox, contain deactivated viruses. The reproductive mechanism in these viruses has been disabled, but they still cause the human body to produce antibodies that prevent subsequent infection by the live form of the virus.

My worry with phage research is that a truly scary pathogenic virus could unwittingly be let loose on the human population. I would rather research focus on how bacteria become pathogenic, and how to stop pathogenic strains from spreading. Research should also work out which catalysts enable pathogens to multiply. There is less likelihood of these kinds of approaches producing unaccounted for problems.

Some Viruses Are Part of Our Symbiote

There are certain viruses that can be called members of the human symbiote. Herpes simplex is one of them, affecting about 95 per cent of the human population. This virus can cause cold sores, but ordinarily survives in latent form in the human body. Occasionally, a trigger event occurs, which causes it to become more virulent, and this is when cold sores appear. No one knows what the exact trigger mechanism is, but there is some evidence that stress could be a trigger. Scientists have only recently understood why these viruses persist in the body, and why the body tolerates them. Apparently they are a real benefit to the human host, as they provide us with immunity against certain bacteria. Herpes simplex has been shown to protect the human host against the bacteria that causes bubonic plague.[6]

The way it does this is by causing the body to increase the levels of a protein called interferon gamma, which is a bacterial growth inhibitor. Because interferon gamma can inhibit all sorts of bacteria, it is reasonable to hypothesize that herpes can protect against other bacterial infections as well.

This is the first time scientists have found that viruses can be members of the human symbiote. This truly changes our understanding of these hardy little strands of genetic material that are technically not even alive. But it makes perfect sense in the context of this book's message. Everything in nature has a purpose, and the symbiote balance is an all-encompassing equilibrium.

There are no viruses yet identified that can be said to be directly beneficial to humans. However, by helping the immune system create antibodies, there are certain viruses that protect us from their more pathogenic cousins. For instance, cowherds who were exposed to cow pox became immune to smallpox, which led to the development of a vaccine for smallpox.

What is truly stunning is that for all the technological advances that have occurred in our world, we still do not understand the common cold virus. Why is it that some strains of it cause symptoms and others don't? How does it spread exactly? Is it possible to turn off the immune response (which causes the symptoms) and still fight the virus? Do viruses serve a meaningful role in evolution?

One thing is an observable fact. The more easily spreadable the virus, the less fatal it appears to be to the human host. Thus the common cold virus, the chicken pox virus, the herpes simplex virus and various rotaviruses and noroviruses spread easily through the human population but are not dangerous to otherwise healthy individuals.

This is not to say that virulently communicable strains of deadly viruses are not possible; they are merely rare. The 'Spanish influenza' virus belongs in this category, which is reputed to have killed millions in the 1920s. But we have not seen a pandemic like the Spanish flu in almost ninety years, despite the vast global reach and the opportunity for viruses to spread at the speed that a passenger jet can travel around the world.

Viruses are also an evolutionary machine, in that they

constantly mutate and adapt, which makes them hard to fight against. However, humans possess not just one but two evolutionary machines, their immune systems and their bacterial/viral symbiote, both of which are good at presenting multiple defences to invading pathogens. Once a virus gets past the symbiote, it is time for the immune system to identify it and launch an appropriate response. Scientists now believe that many cancers are caused by viruses. Certainly, cervical cancer in women is caused by the human papillomavirus (HPV), and today there is a great debate in public health about whether to compulsorily immunize teenage girls against HPV, since a significant portion of them are sexually active and likely to be exposed to HPV as a result.

There is a host of non-specific illnesses that are caused by viruses. The Epstein-Barr virus is linked to chronic fatigue syndrome. Mononucleosis is another viral illness that causes an extended period of fatigue. Eventually, our understanding of viruses will improve to the extent that we can identify the root agent of illnesses.

Every organism has a dormant state. Animals sleep, bacteria also go through a slow stage when they replicate less quickly. Even plants have dormant phases when they are 'resting'. It used to be thought that sleep was the exclusive preserve of organisms with a brain, and somehow it was the brain that needed this 'down time' to rejuvenate. Scientists have done a lot of work on sleep, but most of it has been done in neuroscience labs, trying to understand what happens when we sleep, and why we need it.

As I said in the beginning of this book, the large human brain full of interconnected neurons is an evolutionary accident, and evolution is not about progress but about adapting to a particular set of environmental variables. It is not a surprise then that sleep is not just about the brain; it is about the whole body and indeed about the symbiote as well.

Scientists have recently shown that people who are short on sleep tend to develop more cold symptoms.[7] Many of us know anecdotally that when we are stressed or short on sleep we tend to get sicker, but now there is actual proof. Clearly something is happening during the sleep cycle that rejuvenates the immune system. The immune system needs some down time, and cortisol prevents the immune system from getting this down time. A lack of sleep appears to work in the same way; it prevents the immune system from receiving proper maintenance, and places it under great stress. It is a bit like the watch-tower guard who has not been allowed to sleep properly; he is less likely to be fully alert.

But what about the symbiote? Yes, the symbiote also goes through a dormant period. In the sleep phase, the body's metabolic processes slow down – the stomach is empty from having processed the evening meal so the gut bacteria are quiet, there is less sweating so the skin symbiote replicates less, and the body's core temperature falls, which is a signal for many of the symbiote bacteria to slow down their metabolism as well. What does this mean for good health? Given that symbiote bacteria seem to have a huge and as yet undiscovered role as catalysts in regulating hormones and other secretions in the body, it makes sense that the symbiote too should have rhythms synchronized to the body.

We all have a certain ideal temperature range within which our body functions optimally. This range is higher during the day than at night, which is the reason why we end up sweating more at night even if the temperature is just slightly above our comfort zone; the body tries to cool down by releasing moisture, which cools the body as it evaporates.

Often, insomnia can be treated by lowering the bedroom temperature a little, and making the room dark and quiet. To these three things, I add the ultimate jetlag cure – do a forty-five minute cardio workout about three hours before you wish to fall asleep.

7

ALLERGIES – ON THE PERILS OF STANDING ARMIES

Jamal was a gorgeous little baby, and his parents loved him very much. There was only one problem in his young life – his allergies. He was prone to asthma, and was allergic to all kinds of things – nuts, dust, eggs, wheat, you name it. His parents kept the house spotless in order to avoid aggravating Jamal's allergies. The doctors had no idea why some babies have severe allergies and told Jamal's parents that as he got older many of the allergies would likely disappear on their own, but they could not be sure.

Jamal's parents searched the internet for all kinds of solutions. Finally they decided to get a little puppy as a pet. Jamal is now a toddler and his allergies remain, but there is a massive improvement and he is no longer asthmatic.

There is an ever growing body of evidence that having a dog reduces the incidence of allergies in children. No one knows exactly why, but the most likely explanation is that dogs toughen up the immune system, making it less sensitive to benign proteins, such as those found in tree nuts or dust mites.

The title of this chapter is 'On the Perils of Standing Armies' and a tale from ancient history is a wonderful analogy to what happens in the human body. The ancient Romans knew that the success and growth of the Roman Empire depended on a huge standing army. But a standing army is expensive and it is dangerous to its own civilian government. The reason was that a big army, even one that was their own, would invariably be loyal to one general or another, and would be a big destabilizing force on Roman society if allowed to come too close to the city. To keep the army from becoming a threat to the government, the Roman army was not permitted to cross the Rubicon river, which was 200 miles north of the city and marked the border with Roman Gaul. Any general who crossed the river with his soldiers was seen as rebellious, and the punishment was death.

Our immune system is a big standing army, defending the body against all manner of pathogens. It needs to keep fighting against something or the other in order to maintain fitness. Therefore this immune system is calibrated according to the environment it faces. If you live in a tropical country with lots of potential pathogens in the air, water and soil, the immune system vigorously defends the body against any organism that is not adapted to the human symbiote. But if you put yourself in a sterile environment for a significant length of time, the immune system starts looking for 'enemies' that may not be enemies at all.

The human immune system is an imperfect machine. Its basic method of identifying pathogens is to fight any foreign protein that pierces first the symbiote barrier, and second the skin barrier. We have already discussed how robust the human symbiote is at repelling foreign invaders through a simple process of outcompeting non-resident bacteria for space and food. The skin is also a great second line of defence. Its purpose is manifold, including regulating body temperature, providing a barrier against pathogens, and letting the body's toxins leach out through sweat. But once a pathogen gets past the skin, the proteins on the pathogen trigger an immune response, which comes in multiple stages. The first stage is a fairly general response, like a car alarm that goes off. It can happen whether someone is trying to break in, or merely from the harmless vibrations of a passing car. This response involves sending chemicals called cytokines to the site of the perceived pathogen attack, as well as preparing the area for a more targeted immune response. The cytokines in turn are followed by a bunch of immune cells that perform the various specialized activities involved in fighting pathogens, something similar to armies that have artillery, infantry, supply trucks, tanks and medical support.

The problem lies in the definition of a foreign protein. The immune system does not always know where and how to draw the line between a harmful protein and a benign one. A peanut can represent as much danger as the Ebola virus to an immune system that is not doing its job well. The result is allergies. The generalized immune reaction has also been implicated in a range of immune-related diseases such as asthma, arthritis, lupus, multiple sclerosis, as well as Alzheimer's.

Peanut Allergies and How to Cure Them

Peanut or groundnut allergy is one of the most misunderstood allergies, because the humble peanut has been a staple of the human diet for centuries. Like the potato and the tomato, the peanut is native to South America and has been consumed there since ancient times. It was spread around the world by European traders and has become an indispensable part of the cuisine of cultures across the world. The peanut is a great source of protein, calories and micronutrients like niacin, folate and vitamin E, and it is delicious too. Today, a meal made from peanuts is playing a key role in reducing malnutrition in Africa. Yet the story is not altogether rosy. In a small yet increasing percentage of people, peanuts cause an allergic reaction. And within this group of people, there are those with peanut allergies so deadly that a single half of a peanut could send them into anaphylactic shock and kill them.

So the humble peanut has been banned from school lunchrooms in the US, and even from packed lunches from home for kids. You don't find them on airplanes any more, because an empty wrapper left in a seat pocket could kill an allergic passenger on a subsequent flight. Billions of dollars have been spent on making sure that peanuts are separated and isolated from other foods so that those who are allergic do not inadvertently come into contact with them. For those who are allergic, it is a daily battle to ensure that they don't unwittingly eat a peanut, and they always carry adrenalin injections around just in case they go into anaphylactic shock.

Science does not yet know why the immune system occasionally turns on benign proteins like the peanut. But there are tantalizing bits of evidence. For instance, peanut allergies are unheard of in India and China, where children are exposed to peanuts very early in life. There have also been studies in the UK showing that the later the age that children are introduced to peanuts, the greater the likelihood that they will develop an allergy to it.[1]

There is a strong hypothesis – the hygiene hypothesis – that tries to explain why certain benign proteins are seen as harmful invaders by our immune system. Proponents of this hypothesis argue that the immune system evolved in humans to provide a robust response to food-borne and airborne pathogens, especially those that thrive in the sort of unsanitary conditions that have existed throughout human history. The problem is that in the modern era, at least in the developed world, improvements in sanitation have led to a shortage of real pathogen proteins to fight, thereby leading immune systems to become more sensitive and to pick on benign proteins instead. There is a lesson in this that has broader implications. It is that the human immune system, which evolved on the African savanna, has a strong role to play in fighting pathogens, but at the same time it also needs the pathogens around in order for it to behave in a healthy fashion. If you use other means to destroy all pathogens in the human environment, the immune system fights more and more benign proteins. So the lesson is to let the immune system do its job.

The solution is to desensitize the immune system, by exposing it to all manner of proteins that give it some work to do on a daily basis. In other words, the immune system needs to have something to fight, otherwise it will pick a fight with benign opponents. There is a branch of medicine coming up that tries to do exactly this, called immunotherapy. Immunotherapy has made great strides in the last few years, and now the Holy Grail is in sight, namely, a cure for peanut allergies.

This is brand-new research, but help for peanut allergy sufferers is close. A study was recently published by Addenbrookes Hospital at Cambridge University that shows that kids with peanut allergies can be cured by slowly subjecting them to increased doses of peanut flour over a six-month period.[2] Known as 'desensitization therapy', it works literally by desensitizing the immune system to peanuts over time, essentially teaching the immune system that the peanut protein is harmless. Now I must warn you that this therapy should not be attempted at home due to the deadly nature of peanut allergies. But you can expect that within a couple of years, this therapy will be widely available in controlled allergy clinics, and hopefully peanut allergies will be a thing of the past.

My problem with immunotherapy is that it only deals with trying to cure allergies once they have taken hold. Immunotherapy does not say much about prevention, and the focus of good health should always be on prevention. Keeping the immune system desensitized to everyday proteins is the best way to keep it focused on pathogens.

There are a couple of ways to accomplish this. Sending your kids to play in the dirt works well, because dirt has all kinds of bacteria that are not really harmful to us. This is not to say that your child won't ever get sick if he plays in the dirt, but it is better to risk a small bout of Delhi Belly than to keep your child in an overly sterile environment and risk giving him allergies. Remember, we evolved on the dirt of the African savanna; our bodies are not only perfectly adapted to hanging out in the dirt, but our savanna-based immune system also needs a bit of dirt every now and then to stay in good shape.

There are many ongoing experiments on why dirt is good for the symbiote, and for the human immune system.

For starters, dermatologists at the University of California, San Diego, recently published a paper that increases the body of evidence for the hygiene hypothesis.[3] They found that the staph bacteria that are part of the normal skin symbiote can help wounds heal by releasing a special molecule called lipoteichoic acid that stops outer-skin cells from getting inflamed. What this means is that the skin symbiote is essential for healing after surface injuries, and that in the absence of the skin symbiote there is likely to be excess inflammation and slow healing. What is truly astonishing is that conventional science agrees that staph bacteria are the cause of most skin infections, and in fact the whole point of Broad spectrum antibiotics these days is to fight staph, as we saw earlier.

So the plan of action is clear. At the very least, go home and throw the household disinfectants out with the trash. Do not use disinfectants in the house in an attempt to create an overly sterile environment. By all means keep your home neat and clean and dusted and vacuumed, but without using disinfectants.

Another piece of advice hygiene hypothesis proponents give is to 'get a dog'. From the perspective of the clean police, dogs are filthy animals and a store of germs of all sorts. But dogs have co-evolved with humans for at least 5,000 years and there is a growing body of evidence that their symbiote is fairly compatible with the human symbiote. What this means is that having a dog provides the human immune system with exposure to various microbes that seem to make the immune system less sensitive to benign proteins. If you can't be bothered to take on the responsibility of looking after a dog, do the next best thing and simply make friends with someone who has a dog, and play with it every now and then.

Although desensitization therapy is rapidly becoming an important branch of medicine, not all allergies can be cured by it. Some require other novel cures, and it is worth looking at medicinal systems around the world to see if other approaches to allergies have been more successful.

Let us look at homeopathy and allergies. There is evidence that homeopathy cures certain allergies, particularly allergic rhinitis.[4] The mechanism by which homeopathy works on allergies is fairly straightforward: homeopathic treatment for allergies is really a form of desensitization therapy. The preparations involved are made from common allergens found in the specific part of the world where the patient lives.

There is also evidence that spending time in salt caves can cure respiratory allergies.[5] This is highly intriguing because the mechanism is not clear. Is there a type of bacterial symbiote living in salt caves that reduces respiratory immune response? Or is it the chemical composition of the air in the caves? If the latter is true, you would not expect the beneficial effect to persist once the sufferers have left the salt caves, but the health benefit does seem to persist.

Autoimmune Diseases – Allergies That Are Related to Iron Balance

We have already seen how an excess of hygiene harms the skin symbiote and can lead to all sorts of allergies. But these are for the most part tolerable, and you can always try and avoid the allergens or treat the allergy symptoms. While allergies are an irritant, they are not usually fatal or debilitating. But what about the deep autoimmune diseases, a lot of which seem to affect young women? I am not going to address viral immune diseases like HIV here, but rather diseases where the immune system becomes hyperactive and hypersensitive, and attacks the body's own healthy tissues.

There are many diseases in this category, including lupus, endometriosis, rheumatoid arthritis, Type 1 diabetes and celiac disease. What is stunning is the lack of studies on iron imbalance and these diseases. Looking at lupus, 90 per cent of the sufferers are women of child-bearing age. Of the 10 per cent men, the vast majority also report symptoms of anaemia. According to the medical community, anaemia is a symptom of lupus, but what if it is a cause instead?

The same is true of ulcerative colitis. This is a rare but painful ailment that causes loss of blood through the intestine. No one knows if the initial cause agent is a microbe or an autoimmune disease, but it seems to be genetic in nature.

An extended bout of colitis causes blood loss, which

in turn causes iron levels to fall, resulting in anaemia. But this does not eliminate the possibility that the ulcerative colitis was caused by a lack of iron to begin with, making it a particularly vicious cycle of iron loss causing colitis which causes further iron loss. In this case, the solution is to intravenously inject iron into the blood, so that the patient breaks free of the vicious cycle and her normalized iron then acts to reduce the ulcerative colitis.[6]

The basic premise behind autoimmune illnesses is this: a lack of iron causes the immune system to go into hyper drive. There are reasons for this. A shortage of iron upsets the symbiote because our gut bacteria as well as our skin bacteria need iron to survive just as the body cells do. If there is less iron in the body, there are fewer and weaker symbiote bacteria cells. The symbiote balance is off kilter, which means that the immune system is looking for other enemies, and starts fighting healthy tissue, causing inflammation and a host of autoimmune disorders.

We know from immune-compromised patients, particularly those affected with HIV, how important the immune system is to keep the symbiote balance honest. When the immune system is compromised, normal members of the human symbiote can turn into pathogens and attack the human host. But what about the reverse? Doesn't the human symbiote also keep the immune system in balance? This is logical, and we can clearly see the devastation the immune system can cause when the symbiote is compromised.

These examples point to the role of iron in the body. Too much of it, and the symbiote becomes hyperactive and the immune system is weakened, too little of it and the symbiote becomes weaker and the immune system becomes hyperactive. It is therefore essential to treat the underlying iron deficiency when a patient is suffering from an autoimmune disease.

The deficiency itself can be due to many factors. It could be that your diet has too little iron. Or there may be too little heme iron, which is the easily absorbed kind. Or there could be a deficiency of vitamin D, which plays a key role in iron absorption. Or there may be internal bleeding due to ulcers that is causing iron to leach out. Or periods might be too heavy. Whatever the cause is, the treatment should be to get the iron levels back up.

To end this section on a high note, I refer to the book's introduction, where we spoke about good health being a second order function. Here is a good example of how to apply that second order function to gain good health. It is easy enough to diagnose low iron, particularly if there are symptoms of anaemia. But how does one get the levels back up? Taking iron supplements may or may not help, depending on whether the issue is a dietary iron issue or an iron absorption issue. If it is an iron absorption issue, a lack of vitamin D might be the culprit. But ingesting vitamin D doesn't necessarily help, because it all depends on what form of vitamin D is ingested. If the vitamin D is consumed via milk, that may be counter-productive, as milk actually inhibits iron intake. To top it off, only 20 per cent of the vitamin D in our body is absorbed through our diet. The other 80 per cent comes from exposure to sunlight.

Therefore I prescribe to you, dear readers, my perfectly logical good health suggestion for reducing anaemia: please enjoy a steak, while sitting barefoot and clad in shorts, on a warm beach under the setting sun. Preferably with a glass of good red wine. Now who can argue that isn't a perfect way to good health?

Weak Immune System Diseases – Is Boosting Immunity Ever a Good Idea?

Think of the light of the sun shining on the earth. With minor variations, the amount of sunlight that hits the earth at any given time is constant. Yet half the planet is in darkness at the same time. Different parts of the planet experience different seasons because of the way the earth is oriented at 23.5 degrees in relation to the sun. Despite the harmful radiation that comes from the sun, the planet can sustain life because of the ozone layer that stops the radiation from reaching the planet's surface. Due to all these factors, it is possible for a person standing at a specific point on the planet to experience heat or cold, light or dark, even though the sun's energy is constant.

The immune system is like sunlight, a constant force or

energy. Diet, bacterial symbiote, exposure to heat or cold, exercise, age, sleep, stress; these bodily functions are ever changing in humans. Looking at it this way, it is clear that there is never a situation where there is a need to alter the immune system itself. Instead, the goal should be for the immune system to have an impact on all the other variables in order to achieve a state of balanced health.

In the absence of a healthy symbiote, which in turn can be due to a lack of iron, the immune system's effect on the body is like the sun's rays on the planet without an ozone layer. Just as the sun's radiation would destroy all life on the planet without the ozone layer, the immune system would wreak havoc on the body in the absence of a healthy bacterial ecosystem.

But what about specific illnesses that lower your immunity, such as HIV? There is plenty of evidence that a weakened immune system can itself cause normal symbiotes to turn into pathogens. With the explosion of HIV cases around the world, scientists have seen firsthand what happens when a virus lowers the body's natural immune response. Patients become much more vulnerable to colds, skin infections, tuberculosis and other diseases. The very name HIV is short for Human Immunodeficiency Virus, and it is very clear that HIV is the one disease where your immune system is directly weakened by the effects of the virus itself.

But even in the case of an HIV infection, there is no

prescription to try and 'repair' the immune system. The focus on treatment for HIV is to reduce the viral load through the use of antiviral drugs. Simply by reducing the number of viral particles present in the body, the immune system is allowed to recover and function 'normally' again.

When you see advertisements for medicines that claim to 'boost your immunity', just remember that this is one of the most bogus claims that can be made by any product.

The Dairy Industry and Human Health

Let us move on to one of the most common health problems that we are faced with today, which is in fact a type of allergy. Here is a stunning fact: the majority of human adults are incapable of digesting milk. This is a normal condition known as 'lactose intolerance', leading to symptoms such as nausea, bloating, diarrhoea and gas. Drinking milk puts a strain on the gut symbiote of people who lack the enzyme that helps them digest lactose, and the milk ends up decomposing in the large intestine, releasing gas as well as harmful free radicals.

Children all over the world can tolerate lactose, but this tolerance naturally disappears sometime after age two. The only animal genetically designed to process cow milk is the calf of the cow, if I may state the obvious. So how is it that billions of people are conned into drinking milk every day?

The adult human's ability to digest cow milk – lactose

tolerance – is the result of a genetic mutation that afflicts about 80 per cent people whose ancestors came from northern Europe. This comprises the majority of the population of the US, Canada, Australia, western Europe and parts of Africa.

However, in countries like India, only about half the population has this mutation. When you look at the rest of the world it is an even starker picture. Over 90 per cent of the population of China cannot digest cow milk once they are past the age of two. It is an extraordinary commentary on the state of our civilization that a genetic mutation can lead to the creation of an enormous industry. Think about it: we house cows in barns, pump them with antibiotics and impregnate them artificially with clockwork precision so that they produce milk, which is then sold as 'an essential food that we cannot live without'. And yet two-third of the world's population cannot digest this so-called essential food.

While generations have grown up with television advertisements of kids with milk moustaches, the truth is, milk is just another foodstuff with a controversial background, and it is definitely not essential for human health. Milk is obviously not harmful if you are able to digest it, but like the majority of the global population, if you suffer from any symptoms of lactose intolerance, your health and quality of life would greatly improve if you stopped drinking milk.

There is nothing wrong with you if you cannot digest

milk; you merely belong to the majority of the world's population who should not be drinking milk in the first place. Stop buying into the marketing hype created by the dairy industry. Many health problems can arise when lactose intolerance is not diagnosed, and people spend years trying to figure out what is wrong with them. This condition can develop at virtually any age, and it is one of those things that are so easily missed because doctors in the West do not watch out for it, and milk is everywhere! Millions of people have undiagnosed lactose intolerance, a wholly avoidable condition that causes various symptoms that gut bacteria is blamed for.

8

THE MEANING OF FITNESS AND HOW TO GET THERE

⟨ঃখ্যে⟩

We have talked about the constant interplay of the symbiote and human cells, and how the human body is essentially a balance between multiple ecosystems. More than 90 per cent of the molecules that make up the human body and the symbiote are replaced in a given year. Think about this for a minute. We look more or less the same, have the same consciousness and identity, yet every fourteen months or so there is a complete turnover at a molecular level. It is as if a building was replaced brick by brick every year, but rebuilt according to the same plans. The same is true of our symbiote cells, which are replaced even more frequently than our human cells.

What this means is that very little of our body and symbiote make-up is rigid. Everything is flexible, and enormous changes in well-being could be affected in just a few weeks as new symbiote balances are established. Dr Dean Ornish has done amazing work on how to reverse heart disease in patients through changes in diet and exercise.[1]

We know that most illnesses are reversible if we take the right approach to cure them, yet there is one 'illness' that eventually takes its toll on every one of us. I am talking about the effects of aging. Given that most of the molecules in our body are replaced every year, the human body must have extraordinary regenerative capabilities; so why do we end up as slightly older versions of ourselves each year? Science still has no answer to this question, but it may well be found in the next generation or two. In the meantime, science offers some clues about the aging process. I was in Boston recently and saw a colleague whom I had not seen in two years. In the interim, he had gone on a healthy diet and lost about 40 pounds. I have known this colleague for nearly ten years, and he looked younger than when I first met him a decade ago. Why is it that when obese people lose weight, they also appear to drop a few years from their age?

The answer seems to be a process called oxidative stress. Simply put, human cells use oxygen to create energy. This is a bit like fuel and oxygen burning to create heat energy, except in the case of cells, chemical energy is created. On a side note, the part of the cell that creates this energy using oxygen is the mitochondrion which, as we saw in the introduction, is an ancient bacterium that fused with the archaeal cells to form the precursor to all plants and animals, including humans.

From a health standpoint, what's important is that this process involves the production of reactive by-products called free radicals. Free radicals are balanced naturally in cells by antioxidant enzymes. Despite the bad reputation that free radicals have got in recent times, it is worth noting that in the cells, production of free radicals is not a bad thing. In fact, plenty of free radicals are produced during vigorous exercise, but this is good for you because the body's response is to create antioxidant enzymes that neutralize the free radicals. In fact, once the body gets used to exercise, there is an increased level of antioxidant enzymes that are continually produced, and scientists argue that this is what makes the benefits of exercise last longer than the exercise itself.

This is called hormesis. It is a complex concept but its basic premise is that a small amount of free radicals such as those created by exercise is good for the cells, because the body reacts with an increased defence mechanism that provides a greater net benefit even after accounting for fighting off the free radicals.[2]

The key point here is that exercise is a temporary phenomenon. In other words, it is not a continuous process, because even professional athletes spend most of the day in a state of rest or low metabolic activity, when their production of free radicals goes down to a base level. This means that the production of antioxidant enzymes can keep up with and exceed the normal levels of free radical activity, except perhaps the short period during the exercise itself. When you reduce the amount of oxidative stress in the body, you literally slow down the aging process. This is the reason why fit people look younger; in fact their bodies *are* younger than those of unfit people.

Low RHR, the True Marker of Good Health

The prescription is simple and uncontroversial. Get fit! The various methods of getting fit are beyond the scope of this book, but I will share a simple marker with you. This marker has the advantage of being applicable almost universally to the human population, which is an incredible feat given the diversity of physiologies in our 7 billion-strong species. This marker literally reduces fitness, probability of mortality and indeed good health itself into a single, easily measurable number. No single number is perfect, of course, but this one is better than any other at predicting your health. I am talking about your Resting Heart Rate (RHR). RHR is the heart rate that is present when you wake up in the morning, before you start moving around. You can measure it by counting the pulse on your neck. Simply place your forefinger three inches below your chin on either the right side or the left side of the front of your neck, and find your neck pulse. Count how many beats of the pulse you feel in thirty seconds. Now double the number to get the beats per minute.

For most adults, the definition of desirable fitness is to get to a Resting Heart Rate of sixty beats per minute or less. Elite athletes at peak fitness can get this down to even forty or less, but for most of us, sixty beats per minute will do very nicely. There are groundbreaking studies on RHR as a marker for mortality, and one of them is a study that followed 4,000 Germans between the ages of forty and eighty for a period of twelve years.[3] The conclusions were unequivocal – RHR is a predictor of mortality, and this is independent of whether the people had any cardiovascular risk factors like high cholesterol or whether they were smokers. In other words, RHR predicts your life expectancy after the age of forty better than any other metric that we know of currently.

Another study, this time in the US, followed 600 people over twenty years.[4] This one is just as conclusive and shows that there is a linear relationship between RHR and your predisposition to obesity and diabetes.

The reason this marker is so significant is that we are all individuals with different body shapes, cholesterol levels and genetic make-ups. And we can't agree on a single definition for fitness (is it strength, cardio, stretching?) and how to measure it. It would be truly wonderful if we had a single metric that was almost universally applicable as a measure of good health, and RHR turns out to be this measure. We can actually go further and describe the range of RHR and its relationship to good health.

RESTING HEART RATE AND OUR HEALTH	
RHR (per minute)	**Health Outcome**
Below 60	Good
60–80	OK
Over 80	Bad

This is as simple a table as you will ever see in the highly complex world of heath, diet and fitness. The next question that arises is, how do we achieve an RHR of below sixty? There is no one solution, but all the solutions involve some level of cardio exercise. There are many ways of achieving this, based on whatever activity you find least boring and most fun. In my personal experience, I got to an RHR of 56 through jogging five miles, two to three times a week, at a pace of 9.5 minutes a mile. If you can't jog, you can work on the non-impact cross trainer in the gym for two or three forty-five minute sessions, keeping your heart rate to about 150 during the workout. You can also exercise on the StairMaster, go to an aerobics or spin class, or even try Bikram Yoga, which involves about forty-five minutes of cardio-intensive standing exercises.

The latest research actually shows that the quickest and most efficient way to lower your RHR is through interval training. Run flat out on the treadmill for three to four minutes. Then walk for three to four minutes. Repeat this sequence for six or seven sets. Forty-five minutes of interval training, and you are good to go. And just twice a week is enough.

However, I accept that for many people, especially those who have gone a lifetime without developing an exercise habit, getting the RHR below sixty is a distant dream. But getting it below seventy should be easier. Go for a thirty minute walk in the early morning or evening, four to five times a week. You get your vitamin D, some cardio exercise, and your Resting Heart Rate will drop down to seventy. But whatever you do, do not delay starting an exercise program (after consulting your doctor of course), if your RHR is above 80. The higher the RHR, the worse your health, and the more you are likely to worsen your health in the future.

Learning How to Walk

Have you ever wondered why certain people are called natural athletes? What is it about their physical body composition that makes them better performers at sport? When I was a child, I tried out for the school cricket team. Our geography teacher, who also doubled as our school's cricket coach, let's call him Mr Ancient Tale, was an earnest, roly-poly man. His job was not actually to teach anyone how to play cricket, but to sort out kids who had 'natural ability' from those who did not. He had a series of drills to help him out in his endeavour. How far could you throw a cricket ball? How fast could you run? In effect, the most athletic kids were selected to play for the school team.

Now I would like to ask you a more basic question. Do you remember who taught you how to walk? Of course you don't. Our permanent memories don't go back beyond the age of four, and most of us learned to walk before the age of two. But the main point here is that no one actually taught us how to walk, we picked it up on our own, by watching people.

But there is a big problem with this; there are two ways of walking – the right way and the wrong way. Whether you learn to walk the right way or the wrong way depends entirely on luck, and how the muscle memory forms.

Here are the two broad categories of walking: the first is when you push your legs out in front of you one at a time. People who do this tend to use their calf muscles and their hamstrings to walk. If they want to go faster, they simply increase the length of their stride. In this style of walking, the arms tend to move minimally, as they hardly play a role in the forward motion.

The second category is when you push the ground back with your back heel and drive forward with your front leg. People who do this tend to use their gluteal (buttock) muscles and their quadriceps to walk. If they want to go faster, they simply quicken their pace by taking more steps, and keep their delivery stride the same length. In this style of walking, people tend to use their arms more, swinging them back and forth to drive their body forward.

Of these two categories, only the second category of walking lends itself to an athlete. The reason for this is simple. The two largest muscle groups in your lower body are your glutes and your quadriceps. In other words, these muscles have a far greater capacity to perform work than your hamstrings and calves.

In 2004, I ran the Marine Corps Marathon in Washington, DC. I have been a recreational runner since 1995, running five miles perhaps twice a week. When I turned thirty, I wanted to set myself a fitness goal, and running a marathon seemed like a good target that would lead to a sense of personal accomplishment. What followed then is a tale of how not to train to run a marathon.

I joined ASHA, a local charity in Boston, where ten of us committed ourselves to raising money and running the marathon as a charity venture. The training regimen was simple. I stuck to my twice-weekly five mile runs, and added another run on Saturday mornings. This third run started at five miles, but each week it increased by one mile. It was a four-month training period, and in sixteen weeks, this third run maxed out at twenty-one miles.

Around week five, the problems started. First I developed a serious case of Iliotibial Band Syndrome, which causes shooting pains in the knees. One of my friends recommended I see a podiatrist, who diagnosed me with flat feet and recommended I wear orthotic inserts in my shoes. This in turn caused my ankles and Achilles tendons to hurt, which I simply trained through.

I finally ran the marathon in October 2004, and during the last two miles my right quadricep gave out, followed by my left hamstring. I had to limp the last mile-and-a-half, and came in at just over five hours, which could best be termed as a marginal athletic achievement. Still, it was a great personal achievement for me to have run a marathon and I don't regret it one bit. One thing I could not understand at the time was how so many thousands of people, including eighty-year-old grandmothers and the blokes from 'Save the Rhino' wearing fifty-pound Rhino suits, all finished with better times than me, after all the training I had put into it!

After the marathon, I counted the toll it had taken on my body. I had lost twenty pounds (and I was not overweight to begin with), and most of the muscle mass in my upper body had melted away, while my calves and hamstrings had ballooned to Olympian proportions. I ended up wearing orthotics for the next five years.

You must have guessed by now that I am a category one walker. There wan't a soul in my running club, including the professional coach we hired, who could tell me that my gait was wrong, and that I had no chance of coming in at a decent time, given that my running was all calves and hamstrings. The simple truth is that if I had spent just a few days re-training my gait to use my glutes and quads, and spent some time in the gym doing squats and deadlifts, my marathon training would have been transformed into something close to an athletic achievement.

The solution for you is simple, and you don't have to be a marathon runner to learn to walk properly. Just stand up, wherever you are, and take a few steps, with one hand placed on your buttock. Do you feel the glute tighten and relax as you walk? If the answer is no, then you are not walking the correct way. Just start thinking 'push the ground back', retrain your muscle memory to push back with your back heel (using glute power), take shorter strides, and move your arms back and forth as you walk. You will see the difference right away. If you are a recreational jogger, all the more reason to learn to walk/run properly.

Beware of Podiatrists Selling Foot Insoles

In the summer, I see a lot of people hobbling around Boston on crutches, mainly women, who have one foot in a cast. I have taken to walking right up to them and asking them, 'Ma'am, did you break your fifth metatarsal bone of your foot?' The answer is almost always 'yes'. I then ask, 'Ma'am, have you been wearing orthotic insoles prior to the injury?' And the answer is almost always 'yes'.

Here is a typical scenario: You are a recreational jogger and experience knee pain or shin splints. Someone recommends a visit to the podiatrist. The podiatrist says, 'Ah, yes, you have flat feet, fallen arches,' and recommends custom orthotic inserts. They take a cast of your foot using plaster of Paris, charge you US$ 200, and a few days later you start using shiny new custom inserts that mold to your feet and provide arch support. The knee pain vanishes, so you are thankful to the podiatrist. A couple of years go by, and one summer, you are wearing sandals or flip-flops (where you can't use your inserts), you walk down the street, trip, your ankle gives way, and you end up with a broken foot. What just happened? You got hoodwinked is what just happened.

The simple truth is that human feet developed over tens of thousands of years to carry our weight and help us maintain good posture. Until the development of modern shoes, feet were perfectly muscled and capable of fulfilling all our walking needs. Your foot's greatest enemy is actually your shoe, because it prevents the foot from doing its job properly. If you wear shoes all the time, the muscles in your feet deteriorate, as the foot comes to depend on the shoe to provide support. The same is true when you use orthotics. Your ankle comes to depend on the insert to provide arch support, and as a result, your ankle muscles progressively weaken over time, so wearing insoles becomes a permanent need.

It's like you hurt your leg and the doctor prescribed using a wheelchair permanently. Absurd, isn't it? And yet, millions of people use orthotic inserts on a permanent basis just because some podiatrist sold them custom inserts. It is just as ridiculous.

The real solution to flat feet is to rebuild your arches and strengthen the muscles on your foot. The way you do this is by walking barefoot as much as possible or by getting shoes that provide minimal sole support. This is the natural and correct way of doing things; strengthen your feet, and don't weaken them further by depending on artificial supports.

Athleticism and the Upper Body

Why are some people naturally stronger than others? Of course, there is a genetic component to it, but that is only one aspect. Just as there are two ways of walking, there are also two ways of lifting weights and using muscles in sports.

The first category comprises people who tend to use their shoulder and trapezius muscles when lifting or playing sports. The trapezius or trap muscles are the triangular muscles that connect the neck to the shoulder.

The second category comprises people who use their latissimus dorsi or lat muscles when lifting or playing sports. The lats are the muscles just behind the armpits and below the traps.

Professional athletes belong exclusively to the second category. In your upper body, the muscles that have the greatest capacity to perform work are the lats. If you don't use your lats while doing pull-ups or other weight-bearing exercises, you have zero chance of becoming an athlete, because people who use their lats are far stronger than people who do not.

Consider Bruce Lee, a man who possessed extraordinary strength in relation to his body weight. Just search the web for videos of him performing, and take a look at his lat muscles. Bruce Lee's lats were so strong that he could do fifty one-arm chin-ups. Most of us can't do even one!

In exercising the upper body, it is very important to pull the shoulders down, to stop the traps from firing and performing the work. You will almost certainly need a fitness trainer to show you how to isolate the lats and work them out and to retrain your muscle memory to use the lats, but you will become far stronger by doing so.

Delineating Blood Nutrients from Gut Nutrients

There is a fundamental misunderstanding that most people, sometimes even medical professionals, have about the human body. It relates to the two entirely different systems that operate in the human body. On the one hand, there is the digestive system, which is an open system that enables the ingestion of food and the elimination of waste. On the other hand, there is the circulatory system, which is a closed loop system where blood circulates through the body carrying food, oxygen, vitamins, minerals and hormones from specialized glands to the cells. Food and oxygen are fuel that keep the cells alive; vitamins and minerals are required to keep cells healthy and hormones are simply chemical signals. They can alter your mood, stimulate or inhibit cell growth, and even tell specific cells to die when they are no longer required.

The main point is this: vitamins are only useful to the body when they enter the blood stream. There is a loose correlation between the quantity of vitamin and mineral supplements that are ingested into the digestive system and what actually gets absorbed into the blood stream. This is because blood needs very specific quantities of everything, including food (glucose), iron, hormones, vitamins and minerals, and an excess of these things in the blood is just as bad as a lack. The way the body regulates these nutrients is by storing them in a non-reactive form somewhere in the body and releasing them as needed. For example, calcium is essential in the blood stream to control muscles and nerves and to help clotting, and it is stored in the bones. Fat-soluble vitamins such as vitamins A, D, E and K are stored in the liver. Water-soluble vitamins such as vitamins B and C are not stored anywhere in the body but are excreted via urine, so they need to constantly be replenished through your diet.

Healthy adults in the developed world don't really end up with vitamin deficiency because a) all the fat-soluble vitamins are present in ample quantity in the liver and b) the body will cause cravings for foods containing water-soluble vitamins like B and C if the body runs low. In countries where parts of the population suffer from malnutrition, it is possible to end up with vitamin deficiencies, and many children and adults in rural areas of India have this problem.

There was a time in history when vitamin C deficiency was such a problem that people died from it. This was true mainly on long sea voyages among sailors and passengers, because people ran out of fresh fruit and vegetables and lived on grains and dried meat. Since knowledge about the link between vitamin C and citrus fruits and scurvy was not widespread until about a hundred years ago, this disease was a huge problem on ships. But that's history now!

Getting Egg on Your Face

Did you know that eating egg yolk has absolutely no impact on your cholesterol ratio?[5] In countries like the US, you can buy cartons full of liquid egg white, with the yolks removed. Let me tell you that these products are yet another example of unwitting consumers being completely fooled by a health fad that has no basis in reality.

At first, it seems straightforward. Egg yolks are mainly fat and cholesterol, so eating yolk is bad for you, right? Wrong. Everyone absorbs cholesterol differently, and it turns out that the key determinant of how we absorb cholesterol depends on the composition of our gut bacteria. About two-third of the human population does not absorb dietary cholesterol at all, whereas the other one-third does. Even in people who do absorb dietary cholesterol, the ratio of good to bad cholesterol does not change, which means that there is no risk of increased heart disease from eating egg yolks.[6] Skipping egg yolks is not just a bogus health tip, it's a bad idea. Egg yolks are packed with bioavailable vitamins, essential minerals and other nutrients. Next time, skip the ludicrous and tasteless egg white mix and enjoy a regular, delicious free-range egg without any guilt whatsoever.

The Great Vitamin Con Job and Other Scams

There are entire stores dedicated to herbal cures, vitamins, and other nutritional products meant to 'boost the immune system', 'reduce toxins in the body' and 'improve well-being'. Shelves peddle 'essential oils', which are named so convincingly that the consumers, while buying them, do not want to appear foolish by asking what exactly they are essential for.

These so-called health stores survive on two basic things – one is the placebo effect, and the second is that the basic items that are peddled in these stores are not harmful if taken in reasonable doses.

There was a time a hundred years ago when an entire industry of 'tinctures' sprang up, which were basically various solutions that contained either opium or cocaine. But the damaging effects of opiate use became apparent to health authorities over time, and these substances were banned. Today the most tolerated drug is alcohol, which causes huge social problems around the world, but it is beyond the scope of this book to discuss drug policy.

Health authorities seem happy to look the other way as long as consumer products do not cause actual harm. The placebo effect is well known in modern medicine; countless studies have shown that people feel better when they are told by a person of authority that they are consuming medicine, even if they are taking a sugar pill.

It is not known why this effect exists, but a likely conjecture is that it is linked to serotonin release in the brain. We know that serotonin plays a strong role in emotional well-being. We have seen earlier that playing in the dirt involves contact with a bacterium called M. vaccae that also releases serotonin. Other activities that release serotonin include playing sports and believing strongly in a higher power or god.

Let us look at another category of health food staples – vitamins. The name comes from 'vital minerals' or 'vitality', meaning good health. It is a scientific fact that vitamins are crucial to the good health of the circulatory system and that the lack of various vitamins results in malnourishment of the sort that we see even today in sub-Saharan Africa and other parts of the world.

In the developed world, however, the body and symbiote get plenty of vitamins from the average diet. Topping it up with vitamin supplements is utterly useless. The gut symbiote is not set up to digest vitamins in pill form, and the body is not set up to absorb these pills. There is not a shred of evidence that vitamin supplements have any effect on physiological or symbiote health. The only possible exception is folic acid for pregnant women, which is part of the vitamin B group.

In fact, there is mounting evidence that large doses of vitamins, as in big multi-vitamin pills, are actually harmful. Vitamin A, in particular, is known to be dangerous if ingested in large quantities. But the majority of vitamin-related damage occurs because taking vitamin supplements messes up the body's vitamin absorption mechanism. By training the body to expect large doses of vitamins every day, we are potentially desensitizing the body into absorbing less and less from our guts.

What about resveratrol, the so-called wonder drug? Studies are on-going about the benefits of this compound, found naturally in grapes and red wine, and some other foods. We discussed in Chapter 1 that resveratrol is not bioavailable, meaning that very little resveratrol is absorbed by the body when drinking wine, and that it more likely has an impact on minimizing free radical activity in the gut rather than working its magic in the blood stream. The issue here again is that there is no evidence that resveratrol in pill form gets absorbed at all by the body.

If you trawl through the internet, you will see lots of

salespersons peddling quick-fix pills, and most of them have some M.D. or the other endorsing their products. This has little to do with improving your health other than giving you an expensive placebo. Let me offer you a thought that is far better and far more real than any placebo – at this very second, trillions of symbiote bacterial cells are working hard on your body, keeping pathogens at bay, forming a disinfecting layer around your skin, making natural vitamins for you in your gut, and digesting your food. You should feel really good about that.

As for those pills, until there is more evidence from objective sources, meaning people who don't get paid to endorse these products, stay away.

Candida, the Contradictory Nickname

The word candid means truth, or pure. It comes from the Latin phrase 'In toga candida', which refers to the white cloth that candidates wore while seeking political office. In alternative medicine, Candida refers to a chronic condition caused by a fungus called Candida albicans. Candida albicans does cause illnesses like vaginal or oral thrush, which is not usually a problem unless your immune system is compromised because of AIDS or other illnesses. But there is no scientific evidence that an illness called chronic candidiasis exists, in which your stomach and gut are supposedly full of Candida yeast that live on the sugar you eat.

It is a sad truth that some alternate medicine practitioners feel the need to create mythical illnesses like Candida and chronic Lyme disease which I'll talk about later. In researching this book, the number of bogus claims that I have found, particularly about these two fake illnesses, is staggering. The diagnosis is used as carte blanche to recommend a host of useless treatments. There always seems to be a nutritional supplement involved, which miraculously stabilizes your Candida if you continue to pop a pill three times a day for the rest of your life.

It seems that we are all psychologically susceptible to the idea that taking a pill can improve our health. While this is certainly true for specific illnesses for a specific period of time, the idea that the human body either needs or will tolerate bogus pills for any length of time is laughable. Think about this: the vast majority of people lead completely productive and healthy lives without the need to take a pill of any kind. If you feel that a nutritional supplement will improve your health, first stop and think about the effect of this supplement on your body. Is it a chemical that can alter your symbiote balance? Is it a probiotic? In which case no more than a week's dose should be taken, since probiotics are bacteria that can replicate in your gut. Or is it a completely neutral substance, like a vitamin pill that just colours your urine brown?

Nutritional supplements and pills are unnecessary for most of us. Do not fall into the trap of taking them, and if you must, take them for not more than a few days at the most.

An even more insidious illness is something called 'chronic Lyme disease'. Not only is it an outright fraud, but a diagnosis of chronic Lyme is doubly dangerous because the recommended 'cure' is a long-term course of intravenous antibiotics.

There is a whole ecosystem that has been established in North America with a few controversial medical practitioners who claim that Lyme disease is a chronic condition that cannot easily be cured. As a matter of fact, in most of these cases the patients have not tested positive for the Lyme bacterium in the first place! How can one be cured of a disease for which one has not tested positive?

A detailed discussion on this is beyond the scope of this book, but let me just say that my research indicates that 'chronic Lyme disease' appears to be in the realm of magic realism rather than science. Most important of all, the cure is far, far worse than the disease. Long-term antibiotic use is an absolute disaster from a public health policy standpoint, not to mention the side effects, some of which include blood stream infections caused by using intravenous needles, antibiotic-resistant stomach bugs and deadly bowel infections from clostridium bacteria.

Moreover, this sort of treatment goes against any sense of understanding of the symbiote balance. It is highly likely that what these patients need is some complementary therapy, such as hypnotherapy and cognitive therapy, to rid themselves of these symptoms. The unfortunate thing is that many doctors in Western medicine wield antibiotics or surgery as their primary tools, so they feel more comfortable using these tools rather than sending patients for complementary therapies.

9

WHY GARDENERS NEVER SUFFER FROM DEPRESSION

❧

Angel suffered from depression. Like the silent illness that it is, there were no visible symptoms, but the toll it took on her marriage and her children was very real. Feelings of worthlessness overwhelmed her all the time. She had anxiety attacks, often for the most trivial reasons. Increasingly, she felt unable to go out in public; even a trip to the supermarket was out of the question. She finally moved out of the family home to live with her parents, who were supportive but distraught.

Angel's parents happened to be followers of a guru at an ashram in India. During a visit to the guru, Angel's mother broke down and explained her daughter's condition to the spiritual leader. The guru listened with great compassion and suggested a very simple treatment that involved no doctors and no medication. After returning home, Angel's father had some plant beds installed in their backyard. The spring planting season was just underway, and he insisted that his daughter help him put in the compost and plant the seeds. Angel was perplexed and anxious at first, especially when her father insisted she walk into the garden on bare feet and not wear gloves when handling the soil and compost.

It took less than a week for Angel to start feeling better. When the first seedlings appeared in the plant beds, she felt a kind of joy she hadn't felt in years. Later that summer, she moved back in with her husband and children and converted her own backyard into a beautiful flower and vegetable garden. Her husband installed a hot greenhouse for the winter, as a special present for her. Angel has been free from depression for three years, and she recently returned from a trip to India, where she thanked the guru in person.

Spiritual leaders in India have long been convinced about one thing: it is imperative to move about on bare feet whenever possible. They spend a lot of time outdoors, walking in the dirt and out about in the villages. They feel a connection with what they call the earth goddess by walking around unshod. But there is another connection – one that involves bacteria. There is a specific type of bacteria found in soil and mud that makes the human immune system release cytokines, which stimulate the brain into producing serotonin. The shortage of serotonin, as we know, is linked to depression.

Scientists in England caused a stir when they published

a paper on Mycobacterium vaccae, a species of common bacteria that is found in the soil.[1] M.vaccae are not a permanent part of the human symbiote, because they are what are known as saprophytic bacteria, which thrive only on dead organic matter. But when we spend more time in the dirt, as when playing outdoor sports, we come into constant contact with these bacteria. Therefore, it is a transient but important part of our symbiote. It also turns out that M. vaccae actually stimulate the neurons in the brain into producing serotonin.

There is plenty of anecdotal evidence that people who have active outdoor lives are less likely to be depressed. Scientists try to explain it away by saying that we are social animals, and playing team sports is about being part of a group, and that makes us content and satisfied as human beings. Of course, this does not explain why the same anecdotal evidence shows that rock-climbers, hikers and ramblers also lead lives with minimal mental illness. But the study on M. vaccae bacteria now explains that contact with dirt while spending time outdoors may play an incredibly significant role too.

On the flipside, it is a fact that cold places with little winter sunlight have high incidences of clinical depression and seasonal affective disorder (SAD).

There is so much that we do not understand about the brain. Most of us know or have heard of at least one person who has committed suicide in our larger circle of family, friends and acquaintances. We may or may not know people who suffer from depression, but this is only because most people who are depressed don't shout about their condition from the rooftops. However, depression is a surprisingly common illness.

Most people tend to blame the weather and the lack of sunlight in winter, particularly in temperate zones, as the cause for depression. But according to an old scientific adage, correlation does not mean causality. In other words, just because incidents of depression are high in countries where there is a lack of sunlight does not mean that lack of sunlight is the root cause of depression. For instance, if light and depression were linked, miners would have high incidences of clinical depression, since they spend so much time underground. But there is no evidence that this is the case. While miners are susceptible to a range of other ailments, particularly respiratory ones caused by breathing ore dust, one does not hear about depression as an ailment that exclusively afflicts miners. I would postulate that it is not the lack of light that is the culprit for the high rate of depression in Finland and Seattle, but the fact that people tend not to go out and play in the dirt when the weather is cold, especially if there is snow or ice on the ground. There are well-documented modern professions with higher than normal rates of depression – astronauts, submariners and Antarctic researchers. All three professions have one thing in common – no access to dirt for months on end.

The modern world has made it convenient never to go out. With the internet, television, video games and online virtual lives, people are finding it easier to spend time entertaining themselves indoors. It is no surprise then that the rate of depression around the world is climbing higher.

The solution to this problem is simple – develop a gardening habit early on. You don't need much space to garden, even in the city. There is plenty of information on the internet about gardening in urban spaces, and even a little bit of regular exposure to dirt can reduce the incidence of depression by quite a bit.

Beach holidays serve a similar purpose. It is not so much about people getting a nice tan and feeling good about themselves (although this is undoubtedly true), but the very act of lying on the beach exposes our body to M. vaccae and increases serotonin production in the brain. So we not only feel better, we actually are better! Outdoor tanning is the one occasion where adults get a proper dose of M. vaccae, however sedentary their lifestyle otherwise might be.

Consumption Is a Double-edged Illness

There are clues in human history about another bug that is related to M. vaccae. This one is called Mycobacterium tuberculosis (MTB), and no prizes for guessing the disease caused by this microbe! Tuberculosis has been with humanity since the beginning of our species, and MTB is a normal part of the symbiote, with about one-third of the world's human population carrying it. Mummies from ancient Egypt have been found to have MTB in their lungs.

What is remarkable is that there are so many stories of this disease causing feelings of euphoria among sufferers, even as it wasted them away from within; hence the name 'consumption', which was the common name for tuberculosis in nineteenth-century Britain. Artists were reputed to have become more creative in the throes of this disease, particularly right before the disease killed them. We can only speculate about these historical anecdotes, but it is not unreasonable to conjecture that since MTB and M. vaccae belong to the same genus, tuberculosis might have had the same effect of facilitating the release of serotonin in the brain. This effect could have been even more potent, particularly since MTB lives inside the lungs of the host, as opposed to M. vaccae, which merely comes into contact with the skin when we go outside. The two species are so closely linked that researchers are examining whether M. vaccae can be used as a vaccine against tuberculosis, and in China, a pharmaceutical company already produces an M.vaccae vaccine for this purpose.

Interestingly, the name 'vaccae' is derived from the fact that M. vaccae was first identified from cow dung in Austria. As we saw earlier, cow dung is used as a disinfectant in people's homes around the world, and it now seems that the added benefit of cow dung being full of M. vaccae bacteria makes the people living in these homes feel really good too!

Evolution and Its Purpose

Ever since the human brain became self-aware, there have been philosophers who have wondered about our purpose in this universe and our relationship with our natural world. Isaac Newton provided a framework that solved many of the riddles of the physical world, and Charles Darwin did the same for the natural world. But now this age-old question about purpose has taken on a new twist: is there any purpose to evolution? My favourite answer is one provided by the late Stephen Jay Gould, and I quote him here:

'Evolution is not about progress or increasing complexity. Evolution is about a species simply adapting to the available conditions, or perishing. The human brain became large to adapt to conditions on the African savanna, and for no other reason. Similarly, our visual cortex developed to maximize our survival skills on the savanna. Now, once the brain became large, we developed the capacity for abstract thought, and we started becoming aware of the world around us. This does not mean that the point of evolution is increasing complexity, or somehow that all evolutionary roads eventually lead to self-aware creatures. Plenty of organisms evolve in the opposite direction, towards simplicity. Even today, the world is essentially a world of the microbial, and in percentage terms the number of complex animals, especially humans, is minuscule compared to our bacterial cousins.'

We are all part of this natural world, yet we live in a society that teaches us to detach ourselves from the world and view ourselves as separate entities. We are a symbiotic organism of trillions of cells, a living ecosystem with one human brain and one evolutionary system, constantly adapting and changing. The lessons we can learn from our symbiote are many. The main lesson is to look after this important part of ourselves. The second is to be comfortable with who we are. Obsession with physical beauty, or a misplaced sense of what hygiene is, comes into sharp focus when we look at ourselves individually as a microbial collective, and not as some idealized, sterilized model.

We have already discussed the role of the symbiote in preventing pathogen attacks, how to make sure our symbiote does not itself become pathogenic, and how a weak symbiote results in allergies. Now we will proceed to the cutting edge of scientific research, and see how a strong symbiote actually serves to increase mental well-being and reduce the risk of depression. I am not talking about an external bacterium like M. vaccae, but about the body's own bacterial ecosystem.

Kiss Me and I'll Kiss You Back

There are only a handful of chemicals that regulate mood-swings, namely serotonin, oxytocin and GABA. Each one has a symbiote connection. Oxytocin is released while kissing and during sexual intercourse. Both these acts have profound implications for the symbiote, but only one is strictly necessary for procreation.

The human ability to compartmentalize and contextualize is remarkable. The same people who scrub their countertops with disinfectant have no qualms about French-kissing their date. The same people who would recoil at the notion of drinking half a glass of another human being's spit will do precisely that during five minutes of French-kissing!

When you French-kiss someone, you are exchanging your entire mouth symbiote with the other person. Given the dangers of exchanging pathogens, why does it feel so good (meaning, why is oxytocin released in the brain) when this happens? It is clearly not related to procreation, because you can quite easily procreate with someone without French-kissing!

The explanation is that our body symbiote is perfectly comfortable being exposed to another human's symbiote. In fact, this exchange strengthens both symbiotes, as both end up with stronger mouth symbiotes, by essentially upgrading each other with the strongest species. The conclusion is to go forth and kiss!

What Hypnotherapy Can Teach Us About the Symbiote Balance

Earlier in the book, we looked at the six main constituents of good personal health. The interplay between the big six is essentially the key to good health. These are:

1. Our genes
2. Our symbiotic bacteria
3. Our dietary habits
4. Our exercise and lifestyle habits
5. Our emotional state of mind
6. Our immune system

Irritable Bowel Syndrome is a chronic ailment that causes bloating, abdominal pain, discomfort, diarrhoea or constipation. Doctors have a tough time diagnosing it because there are no specific tests for it, but it is a very real illness that affects thousands of sufferers. No one knows what causes it, but the culprits are variously suspected to be a pathogenic strain of bacteria in the gut, a hyperactive immune system, a stress-related illness or changes in diet or lifestyle. In other words, no one knows what it is so it could be related to any of the six big health constituents. This is what I would call a classic health imbalance illness. For sufferers, the big six are clearly not in balance, but doctors don't know where this imbalance occurs.

Now if Western medicine doesn't know what is causing

an illness, you would think they wouldn't know how to cure it. But there is a cure – hypnotherapy. Studies have shown that patients with IBS showed a dramatic improvement – in many cases they were completely cured – by a session of hypnotherapy.[2]

Hypnotherapy has been shown to be effective in all kinds of treatments, from duodenal ulcers to pain management to weight loss. What is astonishing is that more studies are not conducted so that this safe, non-invasive and effective therapy can be brought into the mainstream. Perhaps the lack of enthusiasm for hypnotherapy has to do with a general fear of any form of mind-control. This is ironic because we are bombarded with different forms of mind-control every day (what are advertisements, after all?).

But in the absence of a well-established industry looking after our emotional well-being, it is up to us to take the initiative. Self-hypnosis is effective and easy to learn from any number of resources freely available on the internet. The essential basis of hypnosis is that the power of suggestion is strong and positive, and like the placebo effect, it has a very real effect on health. Through hypnosis, we can perform two important health functions. One, to strengthen our power of suggestion so that we are able to develop a stronger emotional base. Two, to use that stronger power of suggestion to heal ourselves by talking to our subconscious brain and instructing it to heal our body.

The Role of Stress in Health

We had earlier spoken about oxidative stress, which occurs inside our cells, aging them and making us unhealthy. But here we will talk about the stress that is in our mind, and therefore in our body as a whole. In human beings, mental stress comes from many things – work pressures, status consciousness, feelings of inadequacy, persistent inflammation, allergies, not spending enough time outdoors, and a range of other things. But all these causes of stress have one thing in common: they cause the adrenal gland to increase the production and secretion of the stress hormone cortisol into the blood stream. Cortisol increases both blood pressure and blood sugar, and interferes with the body's immune system. In small and irregular doses, cortisol is not only useful but essential, as it helps the body recover after a period of stress. But when the stress is chronic and carries on for long periods of time, the effects of cortisol turn negative.

The second stress hormone that is released during acute stress is called norepinephrine. This hormone is interesting because it has been implicated in turning the symbiotic E. coli into a more virulent form[3] and also stresses out the E. coli into releasing the Shiga toxin, which causes intestinal upsets. This is very interesting, because stress not only affects the body negatively, but also affects the symbiote negatively by turning a friendly strain of the symbiote bacteria into a stressed-out enemy.

Coming back to cortisol, it is clear that it plays a big role in the build-up of plaque in the arteries, and therefore in heart disease. It increases your RHR, which we have already seen is an important marker of good health. There has been some fairly revolutionary work done by Dr Dean Ornish and his spiritual guru Swami Satchidananda on how a change in lifestyle can reverse the progression of heart disease.[4] However, their work focuses on the physiological causes of heart disease and not on the role the symbiote plays, although it is hard to separate the two.

A healthy physiology and a healthy symbiote are mutually reinforcing. In other words, one leads to the other. So, sweat promotes nitrate producing bacteria on your skin, which in turn keep pathogens at bay. But sweat is also associated with exercise. It is logical to see the link between exercise and good health on multiple levels. Similarly, obese people have different gut bacteria from normal people. In particular, they have a higher ratio of firmicutes than bacteriodetes. Firmicutes are known to increase your body's store of adipose fat, which in turn is linked to increased cortisol and heart disease. Changing the ratio of gut bacteria, in conjunction with a healthier diet, is likely to lead to quicker and more permanent results than either strategy alone.

When your symbiote is balanced, the physiological causes of stress are eliminated.

Health Is Written in Your Stars

Whoa, there! Where am I going with this one? Surely astrology has no place in a science-based health book?

Actually there are plenty of things that people believe to be facts which cannot be explained by science. My interest in such things is not to question the veracity of the beliefs, it is to understand the impact of these beliefs on public health. For instance, around half the human population believe in a higher power that guides the fate not just of humanity in general, but each and every individual. If you include belief systems like astrology, the number of believers in non-science is considerably higher.

These belief systems have proven health benefits. These benefits come from the same area of the brain where the placebo effect comes from, and they are at the core of our identity, of who we are.

In many parts of Asia, astrologers play the same role that mental health and relationship counsellors play in the West. Notionally, you go to the astrologer to have your palm read or your stars explained, but in reality, what you get is a good listener and a wealth of advice on relationship, health and career issues. The role of the professional counsellor or the family priest is accepted and recognized in the West as a legitimate profession that provides real value and service to its customers, and astrology has served the same purpose for thousands of years in the East. The stars and the palm and the tea leaves are really beside the point.

Invisible Diseases – Illnesses That Have No Scientific Explanation

Can you get sick just by looking at someone? This question is not entirely frivolous.

Many years ago, I went through a phase where I felt my career was going nowhere, my financial circumstances were precarious, a close family member was going through a divorce that affected me deeply, and I had just moved to a cold and damp country in the middle of winter. It was a classic case of low-status syndrome, a feeling that all my friends were more successful and were getting better breaks in life's lottery. My weight had ballooned to twenty-five pounds over normal, and I was sleeping a lot, nearly twelve hours a day.

I was sharing an apartment with a friend, a jovial, slightly potbellied graduate student who seemed to have no cares in the world. Over the next few months, I decided that I envied my flatmate, and I began to observe his approach to life to see if I could learn anything. What really impressed me about him was that he only had friends who were optimists, positive souls who saw only the good side to everything. Whenever I moped about something to him, I suddenly noticed that my flatmate had some urgent meeting to run to, but when I was in a good mood he always seemed to be around.

One spring evening, he and I decided to take up running as an activity. We went outside and ran for ten minutes to the nearest park, about a mile away, and collapsed on a bench, out of breath. I saw this exhaustion as a penance, a necessary pain to unlock the benefits of running. My flatmate, on the other hand, saw it as an unacceptable consequence of running, and never ran again.

From that day on, I took up running as a hobby. Once I recovered from that initial run, I stepped up the distance quickly to three miles, then five, three times a week. I began to lose weight, and my depression lifted within a month.

But then I started noticing a strange thing. I always felt a little sore after running, generally the day after a run, which was quite normal as I had begun to increase the distance quite quickly. The oddest thing, though, was that my flatmate also began complaining of pain in his calves, hamstrings, quadriceps, his pain mirroring mine. But he had never run after that first day!

He also lost some weight, although the potbelly remained, and he generally seemed fitter than before. By the end of the year, I had lost thirty pounds, found another place to live that had better access to a long river path, and moved out.

Can we really catch someone else's illnesses, even when they are clearly not caused by a pathogen? There are many historical examples that say the answer is yes. In medicine, there are a group of diseases collectively known as mass hysteria syndrome. These diseases can break out in entire populations in villages and even cities, where people exhibit very real symptoms even when there is no bacterium or virus or other pathogen involved.

Humans are highly social animals, and we are hardwired to show empathy towards each other. Joseph Stalin, perhaps the cruellest despot that ever lived, knew this well when he famously said, 'One death is a tragedy, a million deaths is a statistic.' What he meant is that when a person suffers in front of us, we are hardwired to feel empathy and wish to intervene, but when we read about half a million people massacred in the genocide in Rwanda, it feels oddly impersonal and does not evoke the same feelings of empathy.

This characteristic trait of empathy has a powerful effect on our emotions, and we know that it can be manipulated to both positive and negative ends by people who have the ability and tools to do so. After all, the entire business of marketing is to manipulate our emotions to get us to purchase a product. But how does this empathy wave spread from person to person? Let us look at a couple of examples.

In India, road accidents are very common, and if the accident involves a death or serious injury, frequently the driver of the offending vehicle will abandon his vehicle and run away. This is not because he wishes to flee the crime scene – indeed the offender will frequently run *to* the police station – but because there is roughly a one-in-two chance that the crowd that invariably forms after an accident will decide to beat up the driver. Scientists investigated this phenomenon to see what causes a crowd to turn into a raging mob. The answer seems to be that there are always two instigators who rouse the crowd to turn hostile. Scientists have also found that in those first few minutes after an accident, if someone steps up and uses calming words and gestures to placate the situation, the crowd does not turn hostile, even if there is an instigator doing the opposite.[5] In other words, rousing a crowd into violent behaviour requires both an instigator and an absence of cooler heads who speak up.

In another example, the modern behaviourist Derek Sivers presented the results of an experiment that he conducted in a Seattle park. You can watch the brilliant video on TED.com, and it is only three minutes long.

http://blog.ted.com/2010/04/01/how_to_start_a/

In the experiment, a shirtless man (an actor) gets up in the middle of the park in the afternoon, and starts dancing with extravagant moves. People around him are bemused but largely unmoved. Then a second person (also an actor and part of the experiment) gets up and starts dancing, all the while instigating the crowd. Soon, a third person (who is unaware of the experiment) starts dancing, and within minutes a raging crowd has been roused into dancing in the afternoon sunshine! Derek makes the point that the first dancing person is seen by the crowd as a nut. But once he acquires a follower instigator, suddenly his behaviour generates a wave of empathy that ripples across the crowd, and people begin to see him as the leader of a movement.

We see examples of this invisible wave of empathy all over the world. A single overweight girl in a sorority feels depressed and lonely. But once she makes friends with another person in a similar predicament, you end up with a whole group of girls who put on weight together. Harvard professor Nicholas Christakis has found that there is a network effect of behaviour that extends out to friends of friends of friends, in other words, up to three degrees of separation.[6] The empathy wave can be subtle, like a type of handbag becoming popular all of a sudden, or it can be hysterical, leading to bizarre group behaviour. The most recent example is that of the monkey man syndrome in Delhi several years ago. It began with an innocuous news report, saying that someone had claimed to have been attacked by a monkey while sleeping on their terrace. Monkeys are very common in Indian cities, and lots of people sleep on rooftops under the open sky, so it is not implausible in a city of over 10 million people that a monkey might have attacked someone. But what happened next was an amazing phenomenon. People all over Delhi began reporting attacks, and someone decided that it was not a monkey but a hybrid monkey man who was on the hunt at night, attacking people as they slept. Patrol parties were organized, strangers were randomly beaten up by mobs who suspected them of being the monkey man, and entire neighbourhoods went into lockdown mode at night. People continued to report attacks for months, with actual physical injuries including bite marks and scratches.

The story ended as mysteriously as it began. No monkey man was found, and one day the hysteria just disappeared.

Yet another example comes from the US, where there has been a countrywide case of mass hysteria that has been building for several decades – the bogus story of peanut allergies. For a tiny minority of humans, peanut allergies can be extremely serious. The total number of deaths in the US per year from all food allergies, including peanut allergies, is around 200. To put it in perspective, this is roughly the same as the number of people who die in car accidents in the US every two days. Normally, this would not be an illness that caused mass hysteria in schools and PTA meetings, but there is a catch. There is an antigen test for peanut allergies, which has a high false positive rate, something like 5 per cent. What this means is that for every hundred people tested for peanut allergies, roughly five will test positive even if they are not allergic to peanuts, or are only very mildly so.

What we know from basic statistics is that given the two points of data above, the odds of someone who tested positive for a peanut allergy actually being fatally allergic to peanuts is something like 1 in 10,000.[7] So this test is bogus. Yet, when faced with a positive allergy test for peanuts, most parents will join the rabid group of PTA activists who have now successfully banned the humble peanut from schools and daycare centres. This is a clear example of the phenomenon of mass hysteria.

The last example is extremely well known in medical circles, which is the fact that in elderly couples when one partner dies, the mortality risk of the surviving partner suddenly goes up in the following twelve months. There is no pathogen at work here, merely the fact that surviving spouses often lose the will to live, and that in itself has a measurable effect on their risk of dying, even when they are physically in perfect health.

There are several lessons to be drawn from these observable phenomena, where symptoms of disease appear without an actual bug causing them. The first is to acknowledge that medicine does not know everything about our health. The second is to look at modern medicine as an important tool in health, but not as the only one, as there could be other factors at work.

Environment and Personal Health

If you develop a chronic illness, it is essential to look at all the environmental and behavioural factors before trying to find the underlying cause. This is especially true when there is a group phenomenon that cannot easily be explained.

Once upon a time, the mighty Roman Empire stretched from the Mediterranean Sea to the Urals, and all the way down to Egypt. We know that eventually the empire disintegrated and declined, but was there a hidden environmental reason involved?

There is a plausible theory that the Roman civilization declined because the level of water in the Tiber river in Rome fell by about fifty metres over the span of a few hundred years, as the headwaters of the river changed course. If you go to the Palatine hill in Rome today, to the site of the ancient Roman emperor's palace, you can still observe the original seven hills that were part of the city of ancient Rome. In those days, the Tiber divided the hills so that they were islands connected by bridges. Some hills were the preserve of the aristocracy, while others were crowded ghettoes filled with common citizens.

The city of Rome itself was not an agricultural base, so why would the lowering of the water level in the Tiber affect the city? Superficially, you would expect the opposite, that more prime real estate would become available for development as the waters fell, connecting the hills with lots of empty land. However, what seems to have happened is that as the water levels fell, Rome installed pipes to bring water into homes, which is a perfectly logical response from the richest city in the world, and a technological advance that is worthy of praise.

But there was a problem: the pipes were made of lead, which slowly leached into the drinking water.

We know now that slow lead poisoning leads to all kinds of developmental disabilities in children, and an actual decline in brain development. What may have happened in Rome is that over a few generations of slow lead poisoning, the entire city was deprived of its intellectual prowess. It was then only a matter of time before the city fell to outside invaders. At first Rome's own generals from different corners of the empire took the city in successive waves of invasions. Eventually, the civilization and the empire itself crumbled, once the core – the city of Rome – was made impotent by mass poisoning. And all due to the plumbing!

Today, vast stretches of Bangladesh suffer from mass arsenic poisoning as millions of its citizens drink ground water that has high levels of arsenic. Arsenic causes stunted growth and other developmental problems in children. There are plenty of other examples where entire communities were poisoned by the side effects of the industrial revolution. But this book's focus is on individual health and not communal health, so I shall limit the discussion to environmental factors affecting us as individuals.

The basic question to ask when you develop a chronic illness is this: could there be an environmental reason? For example, if you suddenly develop asthma or breathing problems, ask yourself if you recently moved house. Do you now live in a damp flat where mould is a problem? Do you live in a brand-new home where the walls are made of plasterboard of questionable quality? Is your office workspace properly ventilated? Are you not spending enough time outdoors in the fresh air?

But the focus on environmental factors goes beyond what we can see and smell and hear. There are entire fields of study dedicated to harmonious living spaces, most commonly vaastu and feng shui. The premise is that the arrangement of our living space can promote either harmony or chaos in our life. When faced with illness, at the very least it is worth changing a few things around the house or office and seeing if there is an improvement. For example, it is claimed in vaastu that 'fire' lives in the southeast corner of every home. It is therefore said that the southeast corner of the house is ideally suited for the kitchen/cooking. Conversely, the main bedroom of a couple should not be in the southeast corner of a home, because that can increase the propensity for strife in a marriage.

Let's face it, these sorts of things are difficult for the scientific mind to accept at face value. The point I am making here is not to blindly follow anything, even what I have said in this book, but to keep an open mind and be prepared to question everything, including the tenets of modern medicine. At the same time, it is worth doing things that do not have enough scientific proof, because even when the theory is hazy (as in the case of the placebo effect), we know from empirical research that it works in practice. As long as a suggestion does no harm, consider it, because the process of action is itself a form of medicine; it works because action implies an acceptance that something is wrong, and a willingness to do something about it.

CONCLUSION

The New Meaning of Hygiene

This section is called 'The New Meaning of Hygiene' because I want to talk about specific ways to organize your life so that the stability of the symbiote is achieved. If you have come this far in the book, you already know how important a stable and benign symbiote is for good health. Given this, hygiene does take on new meaning, because the purpose of hygiene then is to ensure a symbiote that is fully compatible with our body cells, thereby keeping pathogens and pathogenic strains at bay.

Praveen is a successful young man, a trainee in a financial services firm. He is a dapper dresser, with spotless shiny shoes and a tousled hairstyle so impeccably maintained that it always looks the same. But he has one problem that has been hurting his self-confidence – a rank body odour that emanates from his armpits at the slightest sign of sweat. No deodorant helps for long, be it spray, roll-on or powder. Deeply embarrassed by it, Praveen walks everywhere with stiff shoulders and rigid arms, always keeping his armpits close to his body. This is how I found him one summer mid-morning, when he arrived at my office for a career chat. His body language was unusually stiff for such a smart young man, and I initially mistook his closed arms for defensiveness and arrogance. Towards the end of the interview, it became clearer what the problem was, as he became increasingly nervous and withdrawn, and the odour emanating from the other side of my desk reminded me of the cheese section of an organic supermarket...

Luckily there is a simple solution in Praveen's case. Go to the nearest pharmacy and look for any topical antibacterial ointment. Smear half a teaspoon on each armpit, and that's it! And the best thing is that you just need a single application of the ointment.

Around 1 billion bacterial cells cover every square inch of skin surface. These are organized into thousands of colonies and strains, all specialized according to the part of skin that they cover. The bacterial flora on your hands is very different from that on your scalp or your armpits. Armpit bacteria, in particular, are specialized to survive in the highly saline environment of your armpits and also thrive on the various chemicals secreted by your sweat glands. The main inhabitant is a bacterium called Staphylococcus epidermis. There are countless strains of S. epidermis, and a small percentage of them are aromatic. Once in a while you end up with a highly aromatic strain of bacteria in your armpits, which in the course of doing their job dish out the unpleasant side effect known as body odour. A one-off application of antibacterial ointment kills that strain of S. epidermis, and the next strain that takes its place is most likely to be non-aromatic, since most strains of armpit bacteria do not produce these pungent compounds. Now if BO is caused by other conditions like a carbohydrate-free diet or certain diseases, the ointment is unlikely to have effect, and it is time to visit a doctor to get yourself checked out.

Yes, it is possible to change small elements of the symbiote with relatively simple solutions.

The Point of Washing and Bathing in the 'New Hygiene'

There are only two reasons to bathe or to wash hands. One is to smell nicer and the other is to wash away any pathogenic viruses and faecal bacteria, particularly on the hands. Both are worthy goals, and I for one would never discourage anyone from a refreshing bath or shower. But do understand that every time you bathe, especially with soap, you are washing away large quantities of skin bacteria, so from the symbiote's standpoint, bathing is a strictly optional activity. If we have access to clean water, then it is almost always true that the environs into which we emerge after we bathe are also likely to be free of any stray pathogens, so a bath using clean water is fairly harmless. But please do not bathe in dirty water.

Every year diarrhoea kills over 3 million children around the world, for which the human symbiote is blamed. This is ludicrous for several reasons. First, most incidents of diarrhoea are due to viral infections such as rotavirus and norovirus. Where diarrhoea is caused by bacteria, the causal agents are faecal bacteria, and these are transferred to the hands if you don't wash your hands with soap after defecating and wiping. If you then eat something or feed your child using your hands, this bacteria gets into your (or the child's) stomach, and can cause diarrhoea. Of course, these bacteria are not meant to be on your hands, and are certainly not meant to be ingested. But even when ingested, it only causes diarrhoea, which goes away in a couple of days, provided you are well hydrated.

The reason 3 million children die every year has nothing to do with simply ingesting faecal bacteria, which is not a good idea but certainly not fatal initself. The children die because when faced with diarrhoea, their mothers stop giving them fluids in the mistaken belief that if the child drinks less water the diarrhoea will go away. In fact, the child gets worse and dies of dehydration. Instead of giving the child water, we blame normal human symbiote bacteria for these deaths, and give antibiotics to children to speed up the recovery, with the result that faecal bacteria are now the most antibiotic-resistant strains around.

Sudden Temperature Changes Wreak Havoc on Your Nasal Symbiote

Dress warmly when going out in cold weather. You lose 40 per cent of your body heat from your ears and feet, so wearing socks and earmuffs can dramatically lower your risk of presenting cold symptoms. We have already seen that avoiding cold infections is impossible, but the key is to fight off the infections quickly, without generating an immune response, which causes the symptoms.

Sunlight Is a Great Disinfectant for Pathogens

People who live in homes that get proper sunlight don't get sick as frequently as people who live in dark caves. The simple fact is that most viral pathogens die when exposed to sunlight and the ones that don't become sluggish and inactive. The same is true for many bacterial and fungal pathogens. Additionally, places with sunlight are usually dry, whereas pathogens like damp places. So don't live in a basement if you can avoid it.

Stay Away from Hospitals

Hospitals are nasty stores of pathogens. Hospitals need to be sterile, as surgical procedures are performed within them. They accomplish this sterile environment through massive use of disinfectants and antibiotics. But this comes at a huge cost. The natural world is not conducive to maintaining sterile conditions for long, and the end result is that hospitals tend to be stores of the worst kinds of pathogens which are usually resistant to antibiotics. There are only three reasons to go to hospital – to give birth, to get a surgery and if you have a life-threatening illness. If you must go, try and get out as quickly as possible, and wash your hands thoroughly with soap and water when you do!

Do Not Use Antibacterial Wipes and Disinfectants, Unless You Are Cleaning an Operating Room

Yes, this advice is controversial. But people are constantly confused between bacteria, which are part of our symbiote, and viruses, which have no known benefits and are frequently found in pathogenic forms. Killing ambient bacteria, especially symbiote bacteria, is neither beneficial nor without risk of harm from pathogenic strains that might supplant benign ones. An entire industry has sprung up heavily advertising that every surface needs to be 'disinfected', preferably using their products. Advertisements show armies of evil bacteria on the march, which need to be doused with chemical weapons. Don't fall for this bunkum!

It does make sense to avoid high contact points like elevator buttons in the winter months when viruses are active, but indiscriminate use of disinfectants is ill-advised. At the very least, it is ineffective and, as we have seen in the chapter on allergies, overuse of disinfectants is a likely cause for increase in allergies among humans.

Take These Extra Precautions during Cold Months

In the winter months, colds and flu are a major annoyance. Get an annual flu shot, which offers a fair amount of protection. Try not to touch elevator buttons and door knobs directly with your hands, as these tend to be storehouses for viruses.

Take Care of Your Teeth through Daily Brushing and Flossing, and See Your Dentist Twice a Year

Dental hygiene is an incredibly important component of good health, and not just because clean and attractive teeth increase one's self confidence. A huge part of your general well-being is determined by the amount of chronic inflammation that exists in your body. Bad teeth lead to gum disease, and gum disease is caused by a number of festering open sores in your mouth that cause your mouth flora to interact with your blood stream constantly, causing low-grade chronic infection and inflammation. This infection has been incriminated in all kinds of autoimmune diseases from rheumatoid arthritis to heart disease to depression. Lots of new research is being done in this area, but don't hold your breath. The problem is that this research is not well-funded, because no pharmaceutical company makes money by proving that regular visits to the dentist can reduce heart disease!

Spend Time Outdoors, Play Outdoor Sports and Get Dirty!

We have seen that M. vaccae, a common soil bacteria and a transient member of the symbiote, actually seems to stimulate our neurons into producing serotonin. Make sure you step out into the dirt regularly to take advantage of this natural boost to your mood and creativity.

Good Health Is a Second Order Function!

Always look for underlying causes of ill-health, and don't just focus on treating symptoms. When you look at yourself in the mirror each morning, give yourself a frank appraisal and think about just one thing you can do each day to enhance your health. Think of good health as a moving target, and try and improve your fitness and your habits a little each day. Set yourself little goals; challenge your colleagues to take the one hundred pushups challenge, where you set a six-week period, start from wherever your level of fitness is, and work your way up to doing one hundred pushups in one sitting. Next do the 200 pushups challenge. Try and run a mile without stopping, and if you are already a jogger, train for a half or even full marathon. These little goals in life, particularly when done with small groups of friends or colleagues, will give you lasting benefits.

The New Meaning of Health

We have previously discussed how there is an ecological balance or equilibrium in the human body between the human host and the innumerable microbes that live on our body. The story is actually more complex than that; there is not one but dozens of different states of balance. Think of a staircase with dozens of steps that are uneven in height. Each step in that staircase represents a state of balance in the human body between various microbial species, when different species of microbes are in a certain ratio to other microbes. This state of equilibrium continues until something happens to shake things up. It could be a viral illness that provokes the immune system to go into overdrive, it could be a change of weather or location or diet or a myriad other things. Whatever the cause, the balance is shaken, and a new equilibrium forms in the body, with either a change in the bacterial species or a change in the number of a bacterial species. This new equilibrium has an impact on the human host, sometimes positive and sometimes negative.

An acute illness is when the body is in between these states of balance. Until a new relationship forms between the immune system, the human host and our symbiote, we suffer through a process where our body's resources are being spent on finding a new balance.

A chronic illness is different. Often, it is like being on a broken step on the staircase. Things seem like they are in balance, but this balance does not translate into good health. Instead, the body is stuck in a state of poor health that persists for a long time.

When you think of your health in this way, it is clear that some steps on the staircase are better to stand on than others. Obesity is a state of balance in the human body that can be the result of many things, including genetic factors, a poor diet, lack of sleep, chronic stress and lack of exercise. It is possible to make changes to diet and exercise to reduce the ratio of firmicutes in the gut, which in turn reduces obesity. When we do this, we are literally stepping off the obese balance and onto a different step on the staircase, a healthier step.

The Big Six Constituents of Our Health

The nature versus nurture debate is too simplistic, and needs to be expanded. I'd like to mention once again the six important constituents of our health:

1. Genes
2. Symbiotic bacteria
3. Dietary habits
4. Exercise and lifestyle habits
5. Emotional state of mind
6. Immune system

Biologically speaking, our life is simply an orchestra made up of these six constituents. This orchestra can make the wonderful music of good health when there is balance and harmony between all six constituents. But when the balance is disrupted, it sounds the cacophony of poor health. And yes, we are the conductors of our own orchestra.

Every form of medicine practised in the world today and every doctor agree on one thing – prevention is better than cure. But what is prevention? Prevention is simply a condition when all six constituents of good health are in a state of balance.

This book has primarily focused on the bacterial symbiote because the symbiote has a tremendous impact on the other five constituents of our health.

Looking at the big six, you can immediately see where Western medicine, as well as large swathes of the alternative health remedies industry, have gone wrong. Western medicine sees most symbiote bacteria as potential pathogens while much of the alternative health industry is obsessed with 'boosting your immune system'. Our emotional state of mind is ignored altogether, except when there is an explicit medical condition like schizophrenia or bipolar disorder. Modern medicine and capital are extensively being deployed to decode genes, as if humanity's problems can be solved like a mathematical equation. Our dietary habits have been ravaged by the processed food industry in the name of reducing the cost of food, even though consumers in the developed world already spend only a tiny portion of their incomes on food. As for exercise and lifestyle, this section is in the realm of the consumer products industries. If they had their way, we would all be sitting in a car (which we replace every three years) smoking a cigarette on the way to the mall to buy more stuff. After shopping, we would go to the pub and drink alcohol and then eat a processed meal while watching television, which would, of course, broadcast a program on the sort of stuff that we should buy at the mall, interrupted only by new car advertisements.

But the clues to good health are all around us, if we would only open our eyes and put the information together. The key to understanding the balance between the big six is to realize that making a change in one of them leads to changes in all the others, and a new health balance is formed. When we think of health in this way, we realize that health issues can often be resolved indirectly, and this is something I hope you take away from this book.

When I was at college in the early nineties, my university president was obsessed with rankings. He would proudly show off the fact that our small liberal arts school ranked number one in the Pacific Northwest in one magazine report or the other. At the time, I couldn't figure out why this mattered. Wasn't it enough that we had a great liberal arts program and excellent faculty and a terrific student body? But I know now that rankings do matter.

A liberal arts school is a balance of different groups or constituents. There is the faculty who want higher salaries and an environment where they are able to interact with other high-quality peers. There are alumni who have paid a lot of money for the college degree and whose continued support of the college is important to meet the college's expenses. There are the students and prospective students who will only attend the college if it has a first-class reputation. You can easily see how a high rank encourages high-quality faculty to come to the school, as well as strong students. It also enthuses alumni to give more money to the school, which in turn helps the school achieve a higher ranking. This is what we call a virtuous cycle.

There is also a virtuous cycle concerning our health. The way the big six constituents work is that there are different levels of balance in the human body between them. Within the symbiote bacterial species, there is an optimal health balance, where the multiple species of the human symbiote are going about their evolutionary goals, and in the process performing all the functions that help the body maintain a state of excellent health. If this gets disturbed due to some reason, the symbiote balance changes to one that is perhaps less ideal.

Diet and exercise are clearly the two most important factors in achieving an optimal symbiote balance, and reducing stress is also extremely important. But once you get onto the path of altering the symbiote balance to a less healthy equilibrium, it can easily create a vicious cycle where you slowly spiral down into an ever more unhealthy balance, until finally you are far from the original state of good health. On the other hand, we can start with relatively poor health and create a virtuous cycle of ever increasing better symbiote balance, which in turn leads to improving health.

If you learn to appreciate your symbiote, it will give you better control over your health. From recognizing symptoms of illnesses to curing most common infections and ailments, the symbiote is the key to health. If you do not understand your symbiote, you will be like a beginner chess player who essentially has no hope of staying on the winning side of the daily battle for good health.

NOTES

Introduction

1   http://www.sciencedaily.com/releases/2008/06/080603085914.
    htm accessed on 13/11/12.
2   G. Marcela Rodriguez, 'Control of iron metabolism in
    Mycobacterium tuberculosis', *Trends in Microbiology*, Vol. 14,
    No. 7, 2006, pp. 320–6.
3   http://conciergemedicinetoday.com

1. Knowing Your Bacterial Friends

1   http://www.ncbi.nlm.nih.gov/pubmed/18710465 accessed on
    01/11/12.
2   Shlomit Gorelik, Moshe Ligumsky et al., 'The stomach as
    a "bioreactor": when red meat meets red wine', *Journal of
    Agricultural Food Chemistry*, Vol. 56, No. 13, 2008, pp. 5002–7.
3   K. Puangsombat, J.S. Smith, 'Inhibition of heterocyclic amine
    formation in beef patties by ethanolic extracts of rosemary',

Journal of Food Science, Vol. 75, No. 2, 2010, pp. 40–7.

4   David R. Whitlock and Martin Feelisch, 'Soil bacteria, nitrite and the skin', *The Hygiene Hypothesis and Darwinian Medicine*, ed. Graham A. W. Rook, 2009, pp.103–15.

5   Claire Johnson and Ronald Eccles, (2005), 'Acute cooling of the feet and the onset of common cold symptoms', *Family Practice*, Vol. 22, No. 6, December 2005, pp. 608–13.

6   Richard P. Wenzel and Michael B. Edmond, 'The impact of hospital-acquired blood stream infections', *Emerging Infectious Diseases*, Vol. 7, No. 2, 2001, pp. 174–7.

7   T. Hanawa et al., 'The role of quorum sensing in Helicobacter pylori', *Journal of Germfree Life and Gnotobiology*, Vol. 35, No. 1, 2005, pp.52–5.

8   Tohru Minamino *et al.*, 'A crucial role for adipose tissue p53 in the regulation of insulin resistance', *Nature Medicine*, **Vol. 15**, 2009, pp. 1082–7.

9   Yu Chen and Martin J. Blaser, 'Helicobacter pylori colonization is inversely associated with childhood asthma', *Journal of Infectious Diseases*, Vol. 198, No. 4, 2008, pp. 553–60.

2. Diet, Bathroom Habits and the Symbiote

1   F.F. Rubaltelli et al., 'Intestinal flora in breast- and bottle-fed infants', *Journal of Perinatal Medicine*, Vol. 26, No. 3, 1998, pp. 186–91.

2   M.J. Hill, 'Intestinal flora and endogenous vitamin synthesis', *European Journal of Cancer Prevention*, Vol. 6, Suppl. 1, 1997, pp. 43–5.

3. Nitrogen and Your Health

1   Jimmy T. Keeton, 'History of nitrite and nitrate in food' in *Nitrite and Nitrate in Human Health and Disease, Nutrition and Health*, 2011, pp. 69–84.

2   A.G. Gianoukakis et al., 'Characterization of the anaemia associated with Graves' disease', *Clinical Endocrinology*, Vol. 70, No. 5, 2009, pp. 781–7.

3   T. Sobko et al., 'Gastrointestinal bacteria generate nitric oxide from nitrate and nitrite', *Nitric Oxide*, Vol. 13, No. 4, pp. 272–8.

4   H.J. Roberts, 'Aspartame disease: a possible cause for concomitant Graves' disease and pulmonary hypertension', *Texas Heart Institute Journal*, Vol. 31, No. 1, 2004, p. 105.

5   World Health Organization, http://www.who.int/water_sanitation_health/diseases/methaemoglob/en/ accessed on 13/11/12.

6   Louis J. Guillette, Jr. and Thea M. Edwards, 'Is nitrate an ecologically relevant endocrine disruptor in vertebrates?', *Integrative and Comparative Biology*, Vol.45, No. 1, 2005, pp. 19–27.

7   R.M. McAllister et al., 'Thyroid status and nitric oxide in rat arterial vessels', *Journal of Endocrinology*, Vol. 185, No. 1, 2005, pp. 111–19.

8   Amrita Ahluwalia et al., 'Inorganic nitrate supplementation lowers blood pressure in humans: role for nitrite-derived NO', *Hypertension*, Vol. 56, 2010, pp. 274–81.

9   D.H. Kim et al., 'Effect of Zen meditation on serum nitric oxide activity and lipid peroxidation', *Progress in Neuropsychopharmacology and Biological Psychiatry*, Vol. 29, No. 2, 2005, pp. 327–31.

10 B.D. Hoit et al., 'Nitric oxide and cardiopulmonary hemodynamics in Tibetan highlanders', *Journal of Applied Physiology*, Vol. 99, No. 5, 2005, pp. 1796–1801.

11 Y. Tang et al., 'Nitric oxide bioactivity of traditional Chinese medicines used for cardiovascular indications', *Free Radical Biology and Medicine*, Vol. 1547, No. 6, 2009, pp. 835–40.

4. Iron and Your Health

1 Rogerio Meneghini, 'Iron homeostasis, oxidative stress, and DNA damage', *Free Radical Biology and Medicine*, Vol. 23, Issue 5, 1997, pp. 783–92.

2 Jesse S. Wright III, Rhuzong Jin and Richard P. Novick, 'Transient interference with staphylococcal quorum sensing blocks abscess formation', *PNAS*, Vol. 102, No. 5, 2005, pp. 1691–6.

3 Peter Spiegler, 'Quorum sensing: finding the on/off switch', *Clinical Pulmonary Medicine*, Vol. 17, Issue 6, 2010, p. 305.

4 http://www.independent.co.uk/environment/how-to-regulate-climate-control-2019095.html accessed on 15/11/12.

5 Dennis O'Neil, 'Natural selection', http://anthro.palomar.edu/synthetic/synth_4.htm accessed on 12/11/12.

6 S.M. Merkel et al., 'Essential role for estrogen in protection against vibrio vulnificus-induced endotoxic shock', *Infection and Immunity*, Vol. 69, No. 10, 2001, pp. 6119–22.

7 A.C. Wright et al., 'Role of iron in the pathogenesis of vibrio vulnificus infections', *Infection and Immunity*, Vol. 34, No. 2, 1981, pp. 503–7.

8 US Social Security Administration, 2006 data, http://www.ssa.gov/OACT/STATS/table4c6.html accessed on 14/11/12.

9   A.L. Reingold et al., 'Toxic-shock syndrome not associated with menstruation: a review of 54 cases', *Lancet*, Vol. 1, No. 8262, 1982, pp. 1–4.

10 'AHA statistical update, heart disease and stroke statistics—2012 update', *A Report from the American Heart Association*. http://circ.ahajournals.org/content/125/1/e2 accessed on 14/11/12.

11 Ibid.

12 R. Luengo-Fernandez et al., 'Cost of cardiovascular diseases in the United Kingdom', *Heart*, Vol. 92, No. 10, 2006, pp. 1384–9.

13 T.B. Vaughan and D.S.H. Bell, 'Statin neuropathy masquerading as diabetic autoimmune polyneuropathy', *Diabetes Care* Vol. 28, No. 8, 2005.

14 Ivan Nasidze et al., 'Global diversity in the human salivary microbiome', *Genome Research*, Vol. 19, 2009, pp. 636–43.

15 M.W. Vernooij et al., 'Prevalence and risk factors of cerebral microbleeds: the Rotterdam scan study', *Neurology*, Vol. 70, No. 14, 2008, pp. 1208–14.

5. Learning to Love Our Microbial Friends

1   G.W. Falk, 'The possible role of Helicobacter pylori in GERD', *Seminars in Gastrointestinal Disease*, Vol. 12, No. 3, 2001, pp. 186–95.

2   http://www.ted.com/talks/bonnie_bassler_on_how_bacteria_communicate.html accessed on 14/11/12.

3   R. Plowman et al., 'The socio-economic burden of hospital acquired infection', *Euro Surveill*, Vol. 5, No. 4, 2000, pp.49–50.

4   http://biology.uoregon.edu/people/green/projects.html accessed on 15/11/12.

5   S. Dial et al., 'Use of gastric acid–suppressive agents and the risk of community-acquired clostridium difficile–associated disease', *Journal of the American Medical Association*, Vol. 294, No. 23, 2005, pp. 2989–95.

6   J.S. Bakken, 'Faecal bacteriotherapy for recurrent clostridium difficile infection', *Anaerobe*, Vol. 15, No. 6, 2009, pp. 285–9.

7   P.J. Turnbaugh et al., 'An obesity-associated gut microbiome with increased capacity for energy harvest', *Nature*, Vol. 444, 2006, pp. 1027–31.

8   'An HSUS report: the welfare of animals in the broiler chicken industry', http://www.humanesociety.org/assets/pdfs/farm/welfare_broiler.pdf accessed on 10/11/12.

9   'Putting meat on the table: industrial farm animal production in America', p. 15, http://www.ncifap.org/_images/PCIFAPFin.pdf accessed on 10/11/12.

10 http://www.ers.usda.gov/AmberWaves/September08/Findings/PercentofIncome.htm accessed on 10/11/12.

6. Harnessing Bacteria to Help Us

1   Hitoshi Nishizawa et al., 'Oxidative stress and inflammation in adipose tissue and insulin resistance', *Adiposcience Journal*, Vol. 3, No. 4, 2007, pp. 386–93.

2   R.E. Ley et al., 'Obesity alters gut microbial ecology', *PNAS*, Vol. 102, No. 31, 2005, pp. 11070–75.

3   Patricia Schlagenhauf et al., 'Sex and gender differences in travel-associated disease', *Clinical Infectious Diseases,* Vol. 50, No. 6, 2010, pp. 826–32.

4   'Horizontal gene transfer', http://en.citizendium.org/wiki/

Horizontal_gene_transfer_ accessed on 12/11/12.

5   N. Yutin et al., 'The deep archaeal roots of eukaryotes', *Molecular Biology and Evolution*, Vol. 25, No. 8, 2008, pp. 1619–30.

6   E.S. Barton et al., 'Herpesvirus latency confers symbiotic protection from bacterial infection', *Nature*, Vol. 447, 2007, pp. 326–9.

7   S. Cohen, et al., 'Sleep habits and susceptibility to the common cold', *Archives of Internal Medicine*, Vol. 169, No. 1, 2009, pp. 62–7.

7. Allergies – On the Perils of Standing Armies

1   G. Du Toit et al., 'Early consumption of peanuts in infancy is associated with a low prevalence of peanut allergy', *Journal of Allergy and Clinical Immunology*, Vol. 122, No. 5, 2008, pp. 984–91. http://www.jacionline.org/article/S0091-6749(08)01698-9/fulltext accessed on 8/11/12.

2   'World-first desensitization therapy is "cure" for severe peanut allergy', Cambridge University Hospitals, http://www.cuh.org.uk/addenbrookes/news/2009/feb/peanut_allergy.html accessed on 9/11/12.

3   Yuping Lai et al., 'Commensal bacteria regulate Toll-like receptor 3-dependent inflammation after skin injury', *Nature Medicine*, Vol. 15, 2009, pp. 1377–82.

4   M.A. Taylor et al., 'Randomised controlled trial of homoeopathy versus placebo in perennial allergic rhinitis with overview of four trial series', *BMJ*, Issue 321, 2000, pp. 471–6.

5   M.R. Elkins et al., 'A controlled trial of long-term inhaled hypertonic saline in patients with cystic fibrosis', *New England*

Journal of Medicine, Issue 354, 2006, pp. 229–40.

6   Christoph Gasche et al., 'Sequential Treatment of Anaemia in Ulcerative Colitis with Intravenous Iron and Erythropoietin', *Digestion*, Vol. 60, No. 3, 1999, pp. 262–7.

8. The Meaning of Fitness and How to Get There

1   Dean Ornish, *Dr Dean Ornish's Program for Reversing Heart Disease: The Only System Scientifically Proven to Reverse Heart Disease Without Drugs or Surgery*, Ballantine Books, Toronto, 1990.

2   Mark Mattson, 'Hormesis Defined', *Ageing Research Reviews*, Vol. 7, No. 1, 2008, pp. 1–7.

3   G.B.M. Mensink and H. Hoffmeister, 'The relationship between resting heart rate and all-cause, cardiovascular and cancer mortality', *European Heart Journal*, Issue 18, 1997, pp. 1404–10.

4   Y. Shigetoh et al., 'Higher heart rate may predispose to obesity and diabetes mellitus: 20-year prospective study in a general population', *American Journal of Hypertension*, Vol. 22, No. 2, 2009, pp. 151–5.

5   Many studies have tried to find a link between dietary cholesterol and blood cholesterol. The problem is that everyone has a different response to dietary cholesterol. The key point is that even in those people whose blood cholesterol level increases from consuming egg yolks, the LDL/HDL ratio is unchanged, which means that egg yolks have no impact on cardiovascular disease. This is one example of such a study: Djousse and Gaziano, 'Egg consumption in relation to cardiovascular disease and mortality',

The Physicians' Health Study, American Journal of Clinical Nutrition, Vol. 87, No. 4, 2008, pp. 964–9.

6   J. Gray and B. Griffin, 'Eggs and dietary cholesterol – dispelling the myth', *British Nutrition Foundation Nutrition Bulletin 34,* 2009, pp. 66–70.

9. Why Gardeners Never Suffer from Depression

1   C.A. Lowry et al., 'Identification of an immune-responsive mesolimbocortical serotonergic system: Potential role in regulation of emotional behavior', *Neuroscience,* Vol. 146, 2007, pp. 756–72.

2   R.F. Harvey et al., 'Individual and group hypnotherapy in treatment of refractory irritable bowel syndrome', *Lancet,* Vol. 25, No. 1(8635), 1989, pp. 424–5.

3   M. Lyte, B.P. Arulanandam and C.D. Frank, 'Production of shiga-like toxins by escherichia coli O157: H7 can be influenced by the neuroendocrine hormone norepinephrine', *Journal of Laboratory and Clinical Medicine,* Issue 128, No. 4, pp. 392–8.

4   http://www.pmri.org

5   K.M. Zeitz, et al., 'Crowd behavior at mass gatherings: a literature review', *Prehospital and Disaster Medicine,* Vol. 24, No. 1, 2009, pp. 32–8.

6   Nicholas Christakis, *Connected: The Surprising Power of Our Social Networks and How They Shape Our Lives – How Your Friends' Friends' Friends Affect Everything You Feel, Think, and Do,* Hachette Group, New York, 2009.

7   The calculation is straightforward. For every million people

tested, 5 per cent or 50,000 will test positive for peanut allergy. But we know that only 5 in a million are actually fatally allergic to peanuts. Therefore the odds of someone with a fatal peanut allergy testing positive is actually 5 in 50,000, or 1 in 10,000.